Pelican Book A721
The World in 1984: Volume 2

D0755047

The World in 1984

VOLUME 2

The complete *New Scientist* series
Edited by Nigel Calder

PENGUIN BOOKS

Penguin Books Ltd, Harmondsworth,
Middlesex, England
Penguin Books Inc., 3300 Clipper Mill Road,
Baltimore 11, Md, U.S.A.
Penguin Books Pty Ltd, Ringwood,
Victoria, Australia

First published by *New Scientist* 1964
Published in Penguin Books 1965

Made and printed in Great Britain by
Hazell Watson & Viney Ltd, Aylesbury, Bucks
Set in 9 pt. Plantin

Contents

Human Mind

KNOWING OUR MINDS BETTER

by Lord Brain, F.R.S.

President of the British Association for the Advancement of Science, 1963-4

Considering the complexity of the human mind and brain, twenty years is not a long time for their further unravelment. By 1984, however, we should understand what the brain does when we think. Already the cyberneticists are constructing models of what it *may* do: one obstacle to knowing how it *does* work is the extreme complexity of the interrelationships of the nerve cells (10,000 million in number) and our present ignorance of some essential anatomical and physiological details. If, however, what is important is the behaviour of 'cell assemblies' in the brain, we may expect to learn a great deal about that without necessarily knowing all we should like to know about the behaviour of individual nerve cells. Already the study of how brain function breaks down in disorders of perception and language is beginning to throw light upon how these functions are organized in the nervous system.

We may expect, also, to understand the cerebral basis of memory. Already a certain amount is known about its anatomical organization both in man and animals. We do not know whether, physiologically, it depends upon the organization of nerve-impulses or reversible molecular changes, or possibly both. Animal experiment may well provide the answer to this, with help from the physicists on the mutual relationship between nerve-impulses and reversible molecular structure in RNA molecules. It would be naïve, however, to suppose that 'a memory' is stored in 'a cell': remembering must involve a complex organization of activity in space and time through many millions of cells.

Already we are well on the way to understanding the anatomical and physiological organization of the brain underlying emotion and the instinctive drives, and this should be even clearer by 1984, and enable us to give a physiological as well as a psychological account of neuroses, such as anxiety states and hysteria. The concept of conditioning will have some part to play in this, as well as the study of infant behaviour in man and the primates.

The classification of psychological types should, by 1984, be on a scientific basis. The recognition of inborn temperamental differences is perhaps as old as civilized man, but their classification until very recently has been empirical, or hypothetical. Now there are tests by which these differences can be measured, and as they are perfected they should reveal basic factors which influence personality, and probably their genetic origins and physical correlations. Such knowledge should be of great value in many fields, especially education, where there should also be advances based on a better understanding of the psychology of learning.

The more scientific our knowledge of human nature becomes, the more likely are we to understand the origins of crime, so that by 1984 there should be a more rational basis for the prevention of crime and the treatment of the criminal than our present empirical and manifestly ineffective methods.

Developments in pharmacology should continue to advance our knowledge of the neural basis of mind and behaviour, as well as adding to our therapeutic armamentarium. Psychotropic drugs can make a growing contribution to our understanding of perception, and illuminate the distinction between the subjective and the objective in experience, our emotional reactions to what we perceive, and the basis of our awareness of time. Sensory deprivation will also throw more light on these questions. It is likely that by 1984 we shall understand schizophrenia in both neurophysiological and psychological terms as a disorder of awareness of reality, and we may hope that its cause will also be known. Psychotropic drugs in new and varied forms will doubtless be used, as Aldous Huxley suggested, to enhance and diversify experience. The social problems of addiction, and even of their medical use on a growing scale as 'tranquillizers', will have to be faced long before 1984.

The unconscious mind is at the moment a somewhat confused and confusing concept, having had so many functions thrust upon it by different psychologists, and having even been treated as though it were a single positive entity. But if we accept that consciousness is dependent upon a vast complexity of unconscious physiological processes, which influence our thoughts and feelings, it should be possible, though difficult, to develop a scientific psychology of 'the unconscious'. This would help us to understand the origins and value of certain types of symbol and image, for example in art and religion. Moreover, since it is well recognized that much creativity in science as well as art has an unconscious source, a scientific psychology of the unconscious should investigate what may be termed 'mutations of ideas', and their relationship to the social environment in which they arise – a hitherto neglected field of history and social science.

Knowledge of scientific causes usually leads to increased control over events. Is there any danger that the growing knowledge of the mind will lead to attempts to control human behaviour on a large scale autocratically? This danger may arise in communities where people are either unaware of it or incapable of resisting it, but in general it may be hoped that the scientific freedom which produces this knowledge will act as an effective antidote to its misuse – though our experience of nuclear weapons may justify some scepticism about this.

Finally, what will be the philosophical consequences of the developments which seem likely? In the past, when psychology was purely descriptive and very little was known about the functions of the brain, the brain–mind relationship could be debated only in the most general terms. But by 1984 it should be possible to give fairly complete psychological and physiological accounts of much human behaviour. The problem of how far the language of the one can be translated into that of the other will then assume a new form. Description of the physiological basis of higher mental activities may be possible only in probabilistic terms, and in experimental neurophysiology the intervention of the observer inevitably modifies the observation. The parallel with recent developments in physics is obvious. Already it is clear that the receptors and 'input' pathways of the nervous system perform functions which can be described in psychological terms, and the word 'information' now has physical, physiological, and psychological implications. If information theory can produce a unified system of ideas which will embrace the gene, the development of the nervous system, and the physiological basis of mind, it must surely profoundly influence our ideas not only about mind, but also about life itself.

SCIENCE AND WISDOM

by Professor C. H. Waddington, F.R.S.

President, International Union of Biological Sciences

Will there be an increase in wisdom by 1984? It is certainly not a commodity of which the human race has shown much sign so far of having a surplus. Nor does recent history encourage one to think that it is at present growing at a rapid rate. I doubt if, by 1984, mankind will be *very* much wiser, in general and over the whole field of life, than they are at present. But I am optimistic enough to believe that there are some aspects of human affairs, and important ones, in which greater wisdom will have been so urgently demanded by circumstances that it will have arisen.

One of these is education. The publication of the Robbins Report on higher education is surely a sign that Britain, like other countries, is already recognizing, and will not again soon forget, that the new industrial revolution, of abundant energy and computer-controlled processes, both demands higher educational standards for a vastly greater fraction of the population, and offers them an amount of leisure which can only be fully enjoyed by people educated far beyond the 'three Rs'. The acknowledgement of the vital importance of higher education is a step towards wisdom from which there can certainly be no going back before 1984.

The challenge of the technical developments of the next few decades will, I think, force mankind to develop further wisdom in an even broader field than education – in his attitude to the relation of the individual to society, and of human societies to the rest of nature by which they are surrounded. The pressures will arise from considerations of food-production and of urban living.

Of course it is conceivable that by 1984 we shall produce our food in factories, without animals or plants, exploiting the most far-reaching biological discovery of the last few years, the synthesis of proteins in cell-free systems. Eventually we should be able to manufacture satisfactory foodstuffs in great chemical plants, where masses of ribosomes would be supplied with synthetic amino-acids and long-lived messenger-RNAs, with energy-yielding phosphates produced by irradiating chloroplasts with laser-tuned light of the most effective wavelength. But that technological dream is nearer fifty than twenty years ahead, unless resources are put into these lines of research at something like the level that was used to develop the atom bomb. In 1984 we will probably still be depending on more or less conventional agriculture.

By that time we shall have had to find some way of developing a really productive agriculture in the enormous areas of Africa, South America, and large parts of Asia which are so unexploited at present. And this task will, I think, force mankind to realize that human society lives its life as a part of a delicately and complexly balanced system of natural processes. To convert the African bush into a productive region conducive to civilized living means the creation of a new system of landscape, and one which is a continuous going concern. It is a task of the kind which in Britain was done, in relation to the technology of that time, some two or three hundred years ago at the time of the Enclosures. We need to do some re-modelling to keep up with the mechanization of agriculture, but many other parts of the world face a much more demanding challenge, for a quite radical remaking of the natural world in which their societies are placed. And this can hardly be done without the realization that man must have a more integral relation to nature than that of mere get-production-quick exploitation. This is a central point in the International Biological Programme which is now being planned (see *New Scientist*, Vol. 18, p. 248).

In highly developed countries such as Britain, the more pressing challenge will come from increasing urbanization (not that this will be unimportant in countries like India and the

African states). In global terms, the problem is that while world population increases by about 2 per cent per annum, the populations of sizeable towns increase by about 4 per cent per annum. It has been argued that between now and the end of this century more new urban building will be carried out than in the whole previous history of mankind. Reflect on this point when next you travel home by underground at the rush hour, and ask yourself what social forces have concentrated this mass of people into one region. By 1984 mankind will have been forced to do quite a lot of thinking about this subject.

First of all, I expect that we shall see the development of a whole new applied science, the 'discipline of human settlements', which the Greek town-planner Doxiadis has proposed to christen *ekistics* (from the same root as economics and ecology). At present, the government supports agricultural research with about £11 million a year, and building research with about £1 million. Well before 1984 there will almost certainly be an Ekistics (or Urbanization and Land Use) Research Council, getting a much higher proportion of official support.

And, of course, it will have been realized that the task, in this connexion also, is nothing less than the complete remaking of the setting in which life is to be carried on, the urban or 'megalopolitan' landscape. But here we are faced with more intimate questions than those involved in remodelling the natural environment into something which is enduringly productive. Before we can remake towns or the great urban agglomerations, we have to have some idea what kind of life we want to lead in them. Do we want to use our increased leisure to cultivate individual gardens, to meet our fellows in football, tennis, and other clubs, to go to theatres and picture galleries, or window-shop, or enjoy any of the other attractions of big-city life? Or, more precisely, the problem will be what combinations, in what proportions, do we want of these things? It will, surely, be driven home on us by relentless pressure that the richness of individual life depends to a major extent on constructive enterprises – building of dwellings, workplaces, transport systems, etc. – which are on such a large scale that only society as a whole can undertake them. And society will have the productive resources to do so effectively. The increase in wealth and leisure should, by 1984, have forced us to abandon, as a major source of human effort, the one-against-all competitiveness which we have relied on so much hitherto. We shall have to come to regard an individual as a cooperating element in society, and society itself as part of a functioning system of nature. That can, I think, fairly be considered a step forward in the increase of wisdom.

THE HUMANITIES AND WISDOM

by Professor Richard Hoggart

Department of English, University of Birmingham

It is easiest to predict first what is likely to happen to the humanities *as subjects of study* over the next twenty years.

They will proliferate and extensively subdivide. Scholars will learn even more – much more – from the scientists and applied scientists about the organization and operation of large, co-operative research enterprises. They will use new mechanical and electronic aids to accelerate scholarly projects which up to now have taken a very long time indeed.

With increased prosperity and an increased demand for the opportunity to do graduate work, the number of grants will creep nearer that for the sciences. So there is bound to be a large increase in sheer knowledge within the humanities. I don't mean critical studies of Keats's washing-bills. There will always be some of those, and I imagine the sciences have their equivalents. But a lot of useful research is waiting to be done in the humanities, and on the whole it is likely to be done efficiently.

This process of expansion and subdivision should be well advanced by 1984. Naturally, not everyone working within the humanities will sympathize with it. But the groups which resist will become both absolutely and relatively smaller – a few small university departments where a professor and some kindred spirits have determined to stand fast; or enclaves within those very large departments which are going to be common in the future, departments with five or six professors and thirty or forty other members of staff.

There is a possible related development which seems to me

more interesting. Scholars in the humanities seem likely increasingly to question their rather rigid 'subject' boundaries and to make new combinations and connexions – and so new 'fields' (as some of the sciences have done). One sign of this is the beginning of the erosion of the dominance of single-subject departments within the humanities in the universities. They seem likely to be more and more bypassed, by the spread of the 'Schools' idea (as it is practised or proposed at some of the new universities) and by developments within the field of joint or combined degrees. I am not thinking of degree courses made up by simply putting together two cognate single-subjects, but of courses which, drawing on two or three different disciplines, are conceived and planned as organic wholes. It follows that such courses will not be like the old and often bitty pass-degree courses either. Focal points for such courses can be found in a period or an area or a number of themes – or in a combination of all these. I do not, I think, underestimate the value of single-subject honours courses, and they will remain important. But I am pleased with the new prospects for first-degree work, and perhaps even more for graduate work in a combination of disciplines – and so in new fields.

These seem likely developments within the humanities as subjects of study. But they will not necessarily have much to do with 'the humanities and wisdom', which is my precise brief. What *is* likely to happen here? And (not the same question) what *ought* to happen? In my view, what ought to happen, what badly needs to happen, is, to put it briefly, this: the central imaginative nature of the humanities should be reasserted. At present it is largely going by default, from without and within.

The humanities (I will draw chiefly on my own subject, literature) explore experience disinterestedly, without wanting to *use* it. This is important, but not peculiar to them. The pure sciences share that spirit – at its best a sort of stillness before experience; a stillness which is not passive, but has the composed and disciplined energy of alert apprehension.

The humanities have two peculiarities. First, whatever part of human experience they are exploring they try to apprehend and re-create *whole* – as engaging the intelligence, the will, the emotions, as in time and space ('of this time, of that place'), as heavy with particular circumstance and yet as representative of other times and places. All this is not *argued*, successively; it is re-created so that it is apprehended by the reader simultaneously, as in life. Abstraction from the imaginative wholeness of experience, which is the first essential of other disciplines, usually means failure here.

Second, the humanities ask questions of value about human experience (though not necessarily explicitly). They implicitly seek judgements; not the judgements of a functional morality (Does it work? Is it efficient?), but those of a substantial morality (Is it good? What is the quality of the life within it?). Of course, scientists as people care about these questions as much as anyone else. And science offers incomparable aids to understanding the objective nature of life. But scientists as scientists can say nothing about the quality of that life. Just as obviously, social scientists as individuals care too; and the social sciences have a lot to tell about life in societies. But social scientists as social scientists do not try to assess the quality of that social life.

People who work within the humanities are sometimes evasive or defensively thin-skinned towards science, and they sometimes make excessive claims. But that doesn't alter the fact that the humanities are the only areas in which human life is explored in all its dimensions at once, and in which we at the same time test assumed or proposed moral orders. There can be no quarrel with science here, except through a confusion of terms. When scientists engage in the activity I have just described they are working within the humanities. So it is misleading to talk about two cultures (or three). There can be only one and we all share it when we try to act as fully responsive and valuing individual human beings.

This fundamental characteristic of the humanities particularly needs stressing today. The increasing complexity of societies increasingly comes to seem justified from within itself, its functional morality accepted as substantial morality. As knowledge subdivides, so does our vision of man; we see him, more and more efficiently, as discrete parts and functions; we risk losing the sense of imaginative perspective and wholeness.

No single piece of evidence can be conclusive here. But a lot of them can indicate a trend. So we might think of the common stress on 'adjustment' when one form or another of 'deviant' behaviour is discussed nowadays; and of the comparative lack of attention to such questions as: 'Deviating from what?', 'Adjusting to what?'. Or we could think of the pressure on universities to plan for production, for social needs; and of the relative lack of interest in their function as the critical watchdogs of a society's values themselves. Or we might consider two areas of change in language today: the increasing use of manipulative language (the language of persuasion at all levels) and the increasingly functional nature of common expression. Or we could, more generally, notice that processing of human relations towards a 'virtuous materialism' (one of de Tocqueville's prescient phrases) through the advertisers, the public relations men, the personnel relations people, and the man-managers. Or we could look at the rebuilding of most of our city centres, with straight-sided concrete beehives sticking up vertically or lying horizontally – and ask ourselves what vision of human life, individual or social, they embody. Or we could reflect on the blanched liberalism of much in British intellectual life today, its lack of tenacity and roughage; or on the way in which the arts are increasingly offered – in vast quantities and cheaply – as commodities to be successively consumed, rather than as challenges to our vision of life. The pressure is always, intelligently and kindly, to reduce the buzz of implication in human experience, the hum of difficult but inspiriting circumstance; the pressure is to bureaucratize taste, ideas, and the imagination, to thin out the sense of life.

There is much to be inspired by and grateful for in the changes of the last two or three hundred years. But in the mid twentieth century we seem also to be moving back to a mood which Arnold attacked in his countrymen a century ago. He accused them of habitually confusing means with ends, of admiring manipulation and organization but hating the contemplation of beauty or of first principles. 'Our besetting sin', he said, 'is our faith in machinery.' In 1984 that may sound even more accurate than when Arnold first said it. Certainly its implicit plea for a full, varied, and flexible imaginative life is now, and will remain, as relevant as it ever was.

Health

STRETCHING THE EXPECTATION OF LIFE

by Sir John Charles

Consultant Director, World Health Organization, Geneva

There is a Churchillian saying 'The further you can look back, the further you can look forward'. However relevant it may be to the panorama of history, this formula hardly applies to the forecasting of the world's health in 1984.

Unpredictable discoveries and events may nullify even such medium-range speculation. Who in 1900 would have imagined that the death-rate from typhoid fever in England and Wales which was then 216 per million population would be 16 in 1920 and 4 in 1940? Who in those countries in 1940 could guess that the year's total of 2500 deaths from diphtheria would have fallen to 5 by 1960? Turning to India, who could have foreseen in 1950, when the expectation of life at birth was 32 years, that 1960 would see it increased by 30 per cent, and 1965 by 44 per cent?

Because of the potential changes in circumstances by 1984, the conjectures which follow are submitted with reserve. They cannot be considered as mathematical projections. New 'magic bullets' for the therapeutic revolution like insulin and penicillin will probably be discovered. But that possibility, together with the emergence of fresh virulent viruses, the belated effects of the many carcinogenic substances human beings now encounter, and increased radiation hazards have all been disregarded.

Furthermore, the countries of the world are not contemporaries as regards development. Socially, educationally, and economically they belong to several chronological strata, but for our purposes it will suffice to regard them as members of two otherwise unspecified groups, the 'developed' and the 'less developed'. By 1984, the differences will be smaller, but the world will still not be one contemporary whole. Some of these differences will continue to be found in the field of health.

The inhabitants of 'developed' countries endowed with medical, sanitary, and nutritional advantages can foresee their future. They now survive most of the perils of childhood, and live to die of cancer and cardiovascular disease, accidents, and the conditions associated with the ageing process. Life may be occasionally subject to ill-health, to influenza or other respiratory infections, to rheumatism, to minor mental disorders, and to the various manifestations of the so-called stress diseases. It is a life endured if not enjoyed, and generally lived outside the shadows of serious communicable disease. Will it be longer and healthier by 1984?

In such countries the length of life can hardly go on extending indefinitely. Females in England and Wales already have an expectation of life at birth of 74 years. For men it is 69 years. These expectations may still gradually increase, but the latter years of the individual will not necessarily be favoured by vigorous health. Often it will be a case of 'medicated survival' and frequent resort to the medical care services.

Certain of the killing heart diseases should be partially controlled by personal attention to such factors as worry, diet, and exercise. Prudence with regard to cigarette smoking should cause cancer of the lung to be less menacing to the British male. Screening methods will reduce the female death-rate from cancer of the uterus and perhaps of the breast.

Chronic bronchitis will diminish as urban atmospheres are purified. Accidents will be reduced as the result of preventive precautions on the road, at work, and at home. Respiratory infections may respond to better environmental conditions and to prophylactic or curative treatment. But mental disorders will still remain and, although some will doubtless decline, we are too ignorant of the causation of others to prognosticate confidently about either prevention or cure. A reduction in the working week following the greater use of automation and electronic control will enlarge human leisure, with perhaps ambivalent results. Benefits there will be, but on the adverse side some increase in the neuroses and psychosomatic disorders can be expected. But, overall, we can rely on a considerable degree of improvement in human health.

In the 'less-developed' countries with their burden of disease, and deficiencies in health installations, personnel, education, and financial resources, reliable statistical data are usually lacking. However, the available information suggests birth-rates ranging from 40 per 1000 population to more than 50, death-rates of 20 or 25 or higher, and infant mortality rates which reach 200 or more per 1000 live births. The ranges indicate the differences which exist within the group. These are often countries where two children are conceived so that one may survive, and malaria, tuberculosis, bilharziasis, diarrhoeal diseases, and malnutrition take a heavy toll of young lives. The expectation of life at birth is frequently less than 40 years, which was the experience of the most favoured countries 150 years ago.

This situation is ripe for spectacular change, subject to certain contingencies. Medical and technical advances can deal effectively with some diseases, but success can be frustrated by political instability, by resistance to change, and especially by financial stringency. Again, after progress has been made further achievement may involve additional expensive effort, as the rule of diminishing returns begins to operate. Finally, with heavy pressure on the local food resources due to population increase or bad harvests, malnutrition may occur and be reflected in the health of the community and its resistance to disease.

Yet great progress can be expected before 1984, depending, however, upon economic and educational development. With relatively slender resources much has already been done under the guidance of the World Health Organization. Mass campaigns against malaria, smallpox, tuberculosis, and yaws have all yielded dividends. So, too, have schemes for preventive immunization, nutritional improvement, education, and training, and the active introduction of environmental sanitation.

Under such improved conditions, the first to benefit will be young children and young adults. By 1984 their expectation of life will be materially extended as they become less exposed to the major killing diseases. It may even have increased by 50 per cent, and range from 55 to 59 years. These ages, now expected in Ceylon and Mexico, may become common even in Africa.

The advantages accruing to the middle-aged will be smaller. They will benefit from the developments in the economic and health fields, but with a legacy of ill-health in earlier years their expectation of life cannot be comparable. Some of them will live, as will the majority of their children, into the age groups where cancer, heart disease, mental disorders, and the senile degenerative diseases become prominent. Nevertheless there will be a general improvement in health, and malaria, smallpox, leprosy, and cholera will be as unfamiliar or as obsolete as they now are in Western Europe.

There remains one somewhat unhappy possibility. Agriculture, industrial development, and education have high financial priority, which may restrict the allocation to the health services. The eradication of bilharziasis, a formidable cause of ill-health and loss of working time in parts of the tropical belt, requires great capital expenditure, as do programmes for environmental improvement. Further examples of the resistance of the insect-vectors of disease to insecticides, and of micro-organisms to curative drugs and antibiotics may also occur. Therefore it may be wiser to anticipate that health improvement in less-developed countries may not be continuous, but will be obliged to advance by stages. But this will only delay and not prevent the ultimate achievement.

Hobbes, the philosopher, described the life of man as 'poor, nasty, brutish, and short'. Surely by 1984 these adjectives will need to be modified.

THE THREE GREAT PROBLEMS

by Professor Sir Charles Dodds, F.R.S.

President of the Royal College of Physicians, London

The pitfalls that lie in the path of a prophesy of the state of any science in twenty years' time are especially treacherous in medicine. The means of dealing with a given disease may appear overnight. In two instances, namely diabetes and pernicious anaemia, this has occurred in my own professional lifetime.

If we look at the major medical problems today they fall fairly clearly into two main groups: the various forms of cancer and the cardiovascular diseases. From a quantitative point of view the latter is by far the more important. Malignant disease, by and large, attacks people in the later years of their life whereas cardiovascular disease robs society of people at the most productive stages of their careers.

In every civilized country in the world there are organizations for collecting and distributing money for cancer research. In Britain and America a very great part of the total effort in medical science is devoted to the study of malignant disease on a very broad basis. As biological research presses closer and closer towards the molecular level, it would appear reasonable to assume that, in the next twenty years, some major breakthrough will occur in the cancer field. We must frankly admit that, at the present time, whilst our knowledge of the malignant process has been vastly extended, we cannot even say in which direction the final breakthrough will be made. It would not, however, be unreasonable to prophesy that, by 1984, a solution to this terrible problem will have been found.

If cancer could be eliminated there would be a very profound effect on the practice of medicine in general and particularly on surgery. Assuming that the cure for cancer was effected by some form of medical treatment (which seems likely) then a great deal of surgery in hospital practice would disappear. It is difficult to say how much surgery is devoted entirely to malignant disease, but it is probably over 25 per cent. There would be important consequences for hospital policy, provision of beds, the careers of specialists, and so on.

Turning to cardiovascular disease, research organizations are now beginning to distribute funds aimed at a thorough investigation of the phenomena of arterial disease. For example, the British Heart Foundation, formed last year, has ambitious plans for a full-scale attack on this problem, embracing as it does coronary thrombosis, cerebral vascular accidents, and their complications. One would certainly be rash to predict that arterial disease will be mastered in the next twenty years but, with the added effort, it would seem almost certain that the outlook for therapy and avoidance of the disease will at least be much better than it is today.

Let us assume that cancer and cardiovascular problems are solved. What then would be the great problem of medicine? Most thinkers are obsessed with the problem of the ageing population. It has been pointed out that all the therapeutic triumphs of medicine prolong life, that the future will be burdened with a preponderance of old people in the population, and that we shall be wrestling with that set of difficulties which are grouped together under the term 'geriatrics'. It would seem that the really great problems of the future lie in this direction. If in the past there has been relatively little research in ageing there is now evidence of growing interest and it may well be that in twenty years' time we shall see institutions filled with scientists of many biological disciplines devoting their time to a study of the ageing process.

It has been tacitly assumed that the degenerative changes occurring in the ageing human being and animal are 'natural' processes, yet if we look for the evidence we find that it does not exist. Research in the next two decades may, on the contrary, show that the degeneration is associated with identifiable extraneous causes (possibly including some dietary factor) and that degeneration is not inevitable in the aged human being. Admittedly, there is no evidence for this point of view either, at the present time – but that may be because one has not looked for it. A concentration of effort in this direction, once cancer and cardiovascular problems are solved, should certainly pay excellent dividends.

A VICIOUS CIRCLE OF CHEMICALS AGAINST CHEMICALS?

by Professor Z. M. Bacq
University of Liège, Belgium

Slow and continuous progress, or sensational but discontinuous advances? In medicine, as in any field dominated by scientific development, we can naturally expect both.

(1) Continuous progress in the understanding of chronic diseases (mainly cardiovascular) at the biochemical level, with rapid development of drug therapy of these conditions.

(2) Continuous progress in the control of ageing – not by rejuvenation but by partial inhibition of the process of normal ageing.

(3) Continuous progress in our knowledge of the functioning

of the central nervous system, mainly from the point of view of biochemical pharmacology. The dangerous possibilities of influencing human behaviour by drugs will be used increasingly – to calm down by tranquillizers people who cannot rest mentally or who are afraid of life's difficulties; to prolong working hours; to create unexpected sensations and new psychological situations. Needless to say, in twenty years, just as at the present time, man should have the right to remain lazy and stupid if he wants to; there is no point in increasing the percentage of highly skilled brains. Fresh, normal minds and bodies, devoid of 'complexes', changing naturally from peaceful rest to agreeable stimulating work, will be rare birds in 1984, so rare that they will look abnormal in a drug-conditioned society. Instead of the wide spectrum of sharp and powerful individualities which have built mankind, we shall see a slow tide of eroded characters and castrated personalities.

(4) Continuous slow progress in classical surgical techniques with the help of physiologists and biochemists. In particular we shall see closer collaboration between radiologists, surgeons, and chemotherapists in the treatment of cancers, with an increasing contribution of pharmacology and radiobiology in two directions: in specific increase of the radiosensitivity of tumour cells, and in control by drugs of those cancerous states that follow virus infection.

(5) The first powerful chemical weapons against viruses will be discovered; here, some sensational steps are predictable. But, just as in the case of antibiotics and cortisone, the first large practical use of these antiviral drugs may create a new pathology. Men, like all mammals, carry many strains of viruses which do not show their presence by any pathological sign. The antiviral drugs will not be specific of one particular virus, but will affect a spectrum of viruses, probably including useful bacteriophages that attack bacteria. Massive treatment with antibiotics has created the deadly infection by a common saprophitic yeast, *Candida*. What is going to happen when the natural equilibrium between man and viruses is disturbed? Control of infectious diseases by vaccination must play an increasing part, because of its specificity and its necessity; the speed of transport throughout the world renders the classical

method of quarantine useless – 'quarantine' means forty days' observation.

(6) Sensational developments in grafting; with inescapable consequences. Let us take an instance which is just at its beginning: kidney grafting. When this technique, in some ten years, is as classical as corrections of some heart congenital malformations, the problem will be to have a supply of normal organs. Not everybody who needs kidney grafting will have a generous parent willing to give one of his kidneys. A curious market (or racket) of fresh organs will open. Are you legally allowed to *sell* one of your kidneys, just as you may sell a pint of blood? Is it legal for a surgeon to take organs from a young man or woman some ten minutes after accidental death? Legal difficulties will become numerous because the legal apparatus is conservative and adapts itself too slowly to scientific achievements.

The development of the so-called diseases of civilization seems unavoidable. It will lead not only to endless troubles for medical men in research and practice, but also to psychological and legal complications. Let us take just one case. The control by drugs of reproduction and sexual activity is spreading, because it is needed in order to limit the accelerated growth of the human population on the Earth. Beyond the estimated number of six billion for the year 2000, great troubles must be expected. For the sake of more food, the use of insecticides, fungicides, pesticides, and artificial fertilizers is going to spread and intensify itself in all countries, with the consequence that concentrations of these substances in the water and food may increase up to the danger point. The great luxuries will be pure water from a spring, plants and animals carefully raised by the consumer himself in absence of chemical contamination, fish caught in the high seas away from the coast. Thanks to increasing leisure, men (at least the most active of them) will feel the necessity to become agricultural workers again.

But it is not only a question of food; space is at least as important a problem. If one puts too many mice or rats in a cage, deep psychological and biological troubles arise. Mankind is going to suffer from this cage effect; the noise, the lack of relative solitude, the disappearance of the forests, and the invasion of open spaces and resorts by an increasing concentration of 'tourists' will progressively affect the stability of human behaviour.

Certain steroids which inhibit ovulation in women are widely used; nobody knows at present what are the consequences of a chronic administration of these substances. Temporary sterilization of men is also contemplated. Sterilizing substances are already present in chickens and beef offered for human consumption. Misfortunes of two kinds may be predicted: somatic troubles affecting only the individual and genetic troubles affecting the species.

Many mutagenic substances, introduced not only in the food but also in the atmosphere of the crowded cities, have been spotted and are expected to increase in concentration. The level of the background of ionizing radiations will also increase. Thus, the most precious acquisition of mankind during the evolution of the species, our genetic equipment, is threatened. It is not impossible that we shall obtain, in the near future, a reliable quantitative estimation of this hazard to human health, if a well-planned international effort is decided upon. But in this field research is unquestionably very difficult, costly, and slowly rewarding.

In 1984, new drugs (more or less effective, or totally ineffective or even dangerous) will be advertised in order to prevent possible genetic damage; mankind will enter deeper and deeper in another vicious circle of contamination, using new chemicals to fight the noxious effects of the existing chemicals of civilization.

Intellectual, technical, industrial, or administrative activity associated with health problems will take an ever-increasing part of every nation's income. Balanced budgets are an impossibility in ministerial departments concerned with health (in my illogically developed country, there are five ministries concerned). An endlessly intricate and costly administrative network, in which the patient will lose human individuality and the medical man his spiritual interest, must be foreseen. The work of the medical profession will be purely technical, except for those fortunate enough to find room in some truly scientific department.

CHANGES IN PSYCHIATRIC METHODS AND ATTITUDES

by Professor Sir Aubrey Lewis

Institute of Psychiatry, University of London

Psychiatry has received much public attention in the last two decades and the importance of mental health has been recognized with increasing readiness: it is therefore easy to infer that the demand for more knowledge and effective treatment of mental ill-health will have been impressively met by 1984. But this is to overrate the scientific and clinical gains of the last twenty years, upon which the expectation is based. These gains have been substantial, but not of a kind to justify confident hopes of a 'breakthrough' which will provide a cure for schizophrenia, an effective means of preventing melancholia, or a quick remedy for obsessional neurosis. Sober appraisal of our recent history suggests that research must be our first concern, even though there is room for more extensive application of present knowledge.

Psychiatry benefits from advances in other fields of science and medicine. It is reasonable to expect that, just as general paralysis of the insane has become a rarity through the discovery and use of antibiotics, other forms of mental illness which are expressions of cerebral disease will fade away, with relevant advances in therapeutics. Much research will be concentrated on the study of metabolic anomalies underlying mental illnesses; the range of 'functional' disorders will doubtless continue to be subject to attrition as their somatic pathology is uncovered. This has already happened with some forms of schizophrenia – for example, periodic catatonia, which is associated with anomalies of nitrogen metabolism.

The most recent and impressive incursions of this sort have been into mental deficiency. Technological advances permitting the separation of metabolic products in blood and urine, and in other body fluids, are making possible the recognition of a steadily increasing number of inborn errors of metabolism which, untreated, lead to mental retardation. Phenylketonuria and galactosaemia are instances of how discovery of the biochemical anomaly has led to dietetic measures which can prevent or lessen the intellectual impairment. As more of these metabolic anomalies are shelled out from the general run of cases of mental deficiency, there will be a wider list of preventive measures. A similar erosion of schizophrenia and other congeries will take place, sooner or later followed by measures for preventing these metabolic disorders. A large body of poorly differentiated deficiency and illness will, however, remain.

The study of chromosomes, which has cast much light on 'mongolism' and the inborn enzyme deficiencies associated with defect, will have been carried further, penetrating into their chemical and molecular structure. The application of greatly increased knowledge of the genetic code whereby particular syndromes are transmitted, and of ways of altering it, will perhaps some day permit radical prevention – a more sophisticated form of eugenics, but hardly attainable by 1984.

Other genetic consequences can be expected from changed social conditions. The emphasis on keeping patients in the general community will make it less likely that those with chronic mental illness will be infertile: they will no longer be physically precluded from reproducing because they remain confined for years in mental hospitals. The consequences of nuclear fission have also to be reckoned with. It is as yet impossible to tell whether the hazards of radiation include an increased mutation rate for the genes responsible for manic-depressive psychosis, schizophrenia, obsessional disorder, and mental deficiency.

The psychological element in the causation and treatment of illnesses that have a physical pathology will be better known. 'Psychosomatic' disorders will have ceased to be a specially designated group and a further step will have been taken on the road towards a unitary description and interpretation of vital phenomena, in place of our current dualism which distinguishes between 'organic' and 'functional', or 'somatic' and 'psychological', and has separate languages for their discourse. The concepts and terms of psychology will be closer towards fusion with those of neurophysiology, and there is ground for supposing that we shall by 1984 know a great deal about the chemical and electrical happenings in the nervous system which are responsible for our wakefulness, our awareness of hunger, our memory, our sexual behaviour, and many other psychological phenomena.

We shall also be more selective in our use of drugs. The current flush of empirical enthusiasm for drugs credited with anti-depressant, anti-schizophrenic, or tension-reducing effects will probably have been succeeded (after a phase of severe scepticism, very likely) by sober appraisal of drugs for the administration of which the indications will be narrow and precise. Their mode of introduction may be neither by the mouth nor by injection into the subcutaneous tissues or the bloodstream: recent studies of drugs directly introduced into the ventricles of the brain suggest further possibilities of con-centrated local action.

Another conspicuous line of development is seen in the construction of models derived from information theory, com-puter theory, game theory – and others yet to be propounded. These provide new conceptual frames of reference. The com-puter, now so vigorously installed, will in the next twenty years have led to the production and use of powerful methods of statistical analysis which, in competent hands, will advance abnormal psychology, especially in regard to the complex interplay of forces determining behaviour.

There will be conspicuous changes in psychopathology and psychotherapy. The ambiguities of psychoanalytic theory will have been somewhat clarified, its bold interpretations will have been checked by experiment, and its details and concepts brought partly into line with the findings of experimental and comparative psychology on the one hand and neurophysiology on the other. Freud's prophecy may by then be partly realized:

The deficiencies in our description (of the instinctual processes) would probably vanish if we were already in a position to replace the psychological terms by physiological or chemical ones. ... We may expect it [biology] to give us the most surprising information and we cannot guess what answers it will return in a few dozen years to the questions we have put to it. They may be of a kind which will blow away the whole of our artificial structure of hypotheses.

Psychopathology will be more tightly expressed and more directly related to systematic observation. Sociological studies will have contributed to stricter understanding of the social causes and manifestations of mental illness, as well as to its treatment. Better methods of prenatal and natal care and up-bringing may have manifest preventive value.

Psychotherapy will have moved appreciably towards attain-ment of its ideal aims – a solid theoretical foundation, and com-municable methods and techniques which have a well-demon-strated efficacy, well-understood indications for use, and practical applicability to the majority of those who need them. We may expect shorter methods of treatment, less compre-hensive optimism, and stronger experimental underpinning.

Surgery, in the form of leucotomy, has moved in and out of the psychiatric field within a comparatively short time. Judging from surgery's place now in the treatment of selected cases of temporal lobe epilepsy, and of lesions of the central nervous system or the endocrine system which lead to abnormal be-haviour, its future role will depend on the discovery of further such somatic causes of mental illness: these may not be macro-scopic, and the techniques of implantation and neuronal stimula-tion may be called for. Such techniques are at present for the most part restricted to the laboratory, and ethical considerations have told against their bold application to human subjects. In the next twenty years, however, laboratory studies may well have justified the wide employment of these procedures in some forms of mental disease, for diagnostic as well as therapeutic purposes.

Whether psychiatrists will have extended or narrowed their scope in dealing with social deviation is highly arguable. If the course of events in the last half-century is a guide, they will be asked more and more to deal with criminals, turbulent and disturbed adolescents, and other people who offend against the social canons. But of late there have been onslaughts against this position, and unless psychiatrists can demonstrate that the psychiatric approach to 'psychopathic disorder' and kindred troubles is more efficacious than that of any other professional discipline, it is possible that sociologists (pure and applied) will hold the field, rather than psychiatrists or, for that matter, psychologists. In that case the last clause in the definition of 'psychopathic disorder' in the Mental Health Act 1959 ('a persistent disorder or disability of mind which results in ab-normally aggressive or seriously irresponsible conduct on the part of the patient, and requires or is susceptible to medical treatment') will need to be changed or the term will have to acquire a different meaning.

The Mental Health Act was intended to usher in an era of community care for the mentally ill and transfer of psychiatric energies from the traditional mental hospitals to psychiatric units in general hospitals, outpatient departments, day hospitals, rehabilitation centres, and social agencies. A corollary of this policy was enunciated by the Minister of Health in 1961; he expected that the number of mentally ill patients in mental hospitals would drop by half in the next fifteen years, and the long-stay population would ultimately dwindle to nothing. It is in the power of successive Ministers to bring this about, to some extent, by ensuring that general hospitals have full psychiatric facilities for inpatients as well as outpatients, that social agencies are plentifully helped to develop their services for the mentally ill in the community, and that mental hospitals are not extensively modernized or rebuilt.

The advantages of the total plan have been widely acknowledged; its disadvantages and weaknesses have been less considered. On close scrutiny, some assumptions in the official case have been questioned, especially the premises on which the forecast of mental hospital populations was based, the practicality of adequate community services being built up in a relatively short period, the suitability of psychiatric wards in general hospitals for all kinds of acute mental disorder, and the extent to which the healthy community will consent to the uncertainties entailed by a large number of mentally ill persons outside hospital.

A prediction as to how this will turn out by 1984 is a guess, inevitably coloured by prejudice. Probably the shift of psychiatric care for acute illness to the general hospitals will have taken place; the mental hospitals will have passed through a phase of being unable to attract enough staff – medical, nursing, and social – and will have been reprieved and refurbished after a painful reduction in their number; and enlargement of community services for the mentally ill and mentally defective will have gone forward, within limits set by the availability of suitable recruits and the state of knowledge about effective measures of education and rehabilitation. It will be a well-recognized principle (but one difficult to implement) that the various stages of treatment – from care of the acute illness to social and occupational resettlement – must be smoothly continuous and not, as often now, a jerky series of fresh approaches.

Shortage of staff is likely to be a serious problem, though not particularly shortage of doctors. By 1984 medical students will be getting a much better grounding in the social sciences and in the clinical principles and methods of investigation appropriate to psychological medicine; and much of the work now falling to the lot of the psychiatric specialist will be competently dealt with by the general practitioner, in whose post-graduate training psychiatry will play a large part, commensurate with the frequency of psychological problems.

There will be diverse efforts to combat the fear and misunderstanding which colour people's notions of mental illness. In this, and other measures that are still experimental, it will perhaps by 1984 be an accepted requirement that means of evaluating the efficacy of any new procedure should be built-in when the project is planned. What is good for new drugs is good for new laws bearing on mental illness and defect, and for new social arrangements designed to ameliorate or lessen psychological troubles.

Domestic Life

HOMES OF THE FUTURE

by E. Finley Carter
Stanford Research Institute, California

Domestic life in 1984 will be greatly influenced by new materials which are even now rapidly becoming available. However, the extent of their impact will depend in a large measure upon the degree to which man is motivated to overcome his human inertia and actively seek change.

In spite of great technological progress in many fields, twenty years is only about half the lifetime of a modern dwelling. The average age of dwellings has steadily declined, from being virtually infinite in the days of caves, to hundreds of years for castles and approximately a hundred years for houses built in U.S. Colonial days, to about forty years at present. Therefore, a very large percentage of the population living in 1984 will be occupying dwellings now in existence. This proportion will, of course, vary widely between large centres of population, especially those which have been rebuilt since the Second World War and 'frontier' communities which are now in a state of early development.

New materials will find increasing use in altering, improving, and equipping many of the older homes. Since we are here concerned with the new and emerging trends, what can we foresee in the way of changes? I think we can safely make quite a few predictions based on the availability of new developments and the social patterns which we know are developing.

Of the new homes being built, a greater proportion will be the relatively low- or moderate-priced housing. High-rise apartments and higher-density, low-rise housing developments will likely make up a larger proportion of the total housing inventory as land values increase in metropolitan areas. The proportionately dwindling middle-age group and some of the older generation will buy the higher-priced houses. A good proportion of the younger generation will live in apartments and developments with community facilities. The older generation will tend toward the condominium.

The average home will not increase in size but will become more functional as to location, interior equipment, and décor. The newer home will be designed for individual appearance and mass production. To make these points compatible, architects and industrial designers will have masterminded the integration of core, shell, and modular construction. Servantless living will put a premium on convenience and simplicity of equipment, appliances, and furnishings. New materials can expect quick acceptance in direct proportion to the time, labour, and money they save the housewife. The family will be able to select from a number of models the type of kitchen, bathroom, and exterior finish so that the final package will be a composite of stock components unique to the family taste.

There will be increased effort to reduce on-site labour by transferring it back to the factory. There the assembly process will be streamlined to reduce man hours. With an increase in prefabrication, the construction firms will be better able to put increasing effort into architecture of the home and utilization of materials.

Let us think of domestic life in 1984 in terms of trends and incremental changes as the product of the possible, multiplied by man's will to apply it to meet his desires and needs. The trend will be toward the simple, away from the ornate, toward the functional, rather than the classic. There is beauty in simplicity in a world that has become frustratingly complex.

Automobile styles, gaudy with chrome, tail fins, and fancy grille work which were status symbols a few years ago, are yielding to simple, unadorned lines as more attention is focused on comfort, safety, and general utility. Changes in clothing styles, though gradual and at times retrogressive, also show a trend toward simplicity and utility. The same trend is evident, and will become more so, in buildings and homes. New materials, producible in abundance, will lend themselves to applications where simplicity and utility will not detract from beauty and good taste. Durability will not preclude economy in original cost, yet variety and flexibility will permit change at a reasonable cost.

The ability to create environmental conditions which can maintain ideal climate, pure air, and freedom from noise, will make available to the average home dweller the seclusion and comfort once limited to those who could afford the luxury of travel to nature's resort spots. Special lighting, enhanced by the development of electroluminescent panels, together with radiant heating or cooling and air-conditioning, will bring these comforts within the reach of millions of families. Access to almost limitless information through colour television, facsimile, stereophonic broadcasting, and recordings will furnish cultural atmospheres and permit close contact with current events as well as with areas of the world formerly accessible to relatively few people.

Communications will be ample and economical over long distances. Travel will be fast and relatively low in cost. Television-telephone may reduce the need for shopping trips into congested areas and will permit carrying on face-to-face business conferences and important transactions from one's home – in many instances as effectively as if one were present at a remote office or conference table. A word of warning might here be sounded: the comfort and seclusion of one's home, together with abundant facilities for communicating with the outside world, may bring about a degree of isolation which could limit some of the finer human values that can come only from close association with people.

New materials – the products of ingenious research and resourceful product development – will be in evidence in all aspects of home construction and daily life. Wall and ceiling panels, made of plastic foam sandwiched between thin metals, ceramic, pressed wood, or plastic sheets, will have light-weight, high-insulation properties and good strength. Surface coatings of foil, film, sheet, or spray will be tough, durable, and colourful. Fabrics for draperies, floor coverings, and upholstering, whether chemically treated natural fibres, or woven or non-woven synthetics, will have lustre and beauty, long life, and ease of cleaning and maintenance.

New materials for new devices will play many hidden roles

as well. Packaged power units, whose future availability depends in large measure on present-day materials research, will free many appliances from the limitations of extension cords. Noise abatement and air purity will be enhanced by proportional decreases in the use of internal combustion engines. There will be an increasing use of electrical heating in homes and a corresponding decline in the burning of fossil fuels containing valuable chemical resources. Direct energy converters and efficient accumulators, taking their charges during off-peak-load periods, should improve economy and reduce electric power costs. Solar energy will be put to greater uses. New developments in glass will aid in shielding or transmitting infra-red and heat waves to suit particular applications.

Much of the electric power will be produced from nuclear sources, thus further reducing air pollution from the burning of fossil fuels. Packaged power is already in wide use for flashlights, hearing aids, portable radios, electric shavers, and the like. By 1984 it will also be performing an important role in creature comforts for individuals. Small batteries in the pockets of light-weight apparel made of then-available material will provide well-regulated body-environmental temperatures without the need for heavy overcoats. Larger batteries will furnish motive power for an increasing percentage of vehicular transportation.

With the possibilities of greater leisure both from work and from the carrying out of household chores, interest should turn to cultural development and creative hobbies. The home equipped with facilities for lightening housework, the availability of fully or semi-prepared foods with ready facilities for warming them or cooling them, as the case may be, will allow more time for engagement in study and hobbies which can be both entertaining and creative. Conversation pieces and even status symbols may well be art work, literary compositions, collections of rare books or rare objects, or ingenious devices developed in the studio, library, hobby room, or shop.

I have endeavoured to project these thoughts into 1984 on the assumption that man's spirit, industry, and creative instincts will motivate him to utilize that which is foreseeably possible. His realization may be much greater than herein indicated, or less, in proportion to the degree of that motivation.

Through a better understanding of his fellow man, which can rapidly come about through available information, instantaneous communication, and fast travel, mankind can be released from fears based on ignorance, and the suspicions and hatreds those fears bring about. Accordingly, if his mind and spirit can be directed toward a constructive application of leisure and resources at hand, then what has been said here is just a preview of more wonderful things to come.

A ROBOT ABOUT THE HOUSE

by Professor M. W. Thring

Department of Fuel Technology and Chemical Engineering,
University of Sheffield

As civilization proceeds in the direction of technology, it passes the point of supplying all the basic essentials of life – food, shelter, clothes, and warmth. Then we are faced with a choice between using technology to provide and fulfil needs which have hitherto been regarded as unnecessary or, on the other hand, using technology to reduce the number of hours of work which a man must do in order to earn a given standard of living. In other words, we either raise our standard of living above that necessary for comfort and happiness or we leave it at this level and work shorter hours. In trying to predict the situation of domestic life in 1984, I shall take it as axiomatic that mankind has, by that time, chosen the latter alternative. Men will be working shorter and shorter hours in their paid employment. It follows that the housewife will also expect to be able to have more leisure in her life without lowering her standard of living. It also follows that human domestic servants will have completely ceased to exist.

Both men and women will be working shorter hours and will be educated to choose a creative hobby or activity which they do for their own satisfaction outside their need to earn their living or keep their homes in comfortable condition. I think it can also be taken as axiomatic that human beings will not want

to have completely standardized homes with built-in machines
to keep everything in exactly the same place in every home.
Even if they build completely sealed clean-air boxes to live in
they will still make a certain amount of dirt within them by
their own activities.

It seems likely, therefore, that it will be better in 1984, from
the point of view of human happiness, to have as great a variety
and range of shapes and conditions of homes as we have now.
Yet the great majority of the housewives will wish to be relieved
completely from the routine operations of the home such as
scrubbing the floors or the bath or the cooker, or washing the
clothes or washing up, or dusting or sweeping, or making beds.

By far the most logical step to allow this variety of human
homes and still relieve the housewife of routine, is to provide a
robot slave which can be trained to the requirements of a particular home and can be programmed to carry out half a dozen
or more standard operations (for example, scrubbing, sweeping
and dusting, washing-up, laying tables, making beds), when so
switched by the housewife. It will be a machine having no more
emotions than a car, but having a memory for instructions and a
limited degree of instructed or built-in adaptability according
to the positions in which it finds various types of objects. It
will operate other more specialized machines, for example, the
vacuum cleaner or clothes-washing machine.

There are no problems in the production of such a domestic
robot to which we do not have already the glimmering of a
solution. It is therefore likely that, with a strong programme of
research, such a robot could be produced in ten years. If we
assume that it also takes ten years before industry and government are sufficiently interested to find the sum required for
such development (which is of the order of £1 million), then we
could still have it by 1984.

When I have discussed this kind of device with housewives,
some 90 per cent of them have the immediate reaction, 'How
soon can I buy one?' The other 10 per cent have the reaction,
'I would be terrified to have it moving about my house' – but
when one explains to them that it could be switched off or
unplugged or stopped without the slightest difficulty, or made
to go and put itself away in a cupboard at any time, they quickly

realize that it is a highly desirable object. In my own home we have found that, at first, the washing-up machine was regarded as a rival to the worker at the kitchen sink, but now there is no greater pleasure than to go to bed in the evening and know that the washing-up is being done downstairs after one is asleep. Some families would be delighted, no doubt, to have the robot slave doing all the downstairs housework after they were in bed at night, while others would prefer to have it done in the mornings, but this would be entirely a matter of choice.

It is impossible to predict in detail the shape and mechanism of the robot slave. It might carry its computer and response mechanism around with it and also its source of power; or it might operate with a computer stored in a cupboard under the stairs and the signals and information proceeding along a cable which also carries the power from the mains through the machine moving about the house. In this case it would unwind its cable as it went to a given room and wind it up again when it went back and put itself away under the stairs. It might carry its power, for example, by storage batteries, and have its instructions beamed to it by short-wave short-range electromagnetic waves. The machine would have to be able to move about in a house designed for human beings and would therefore probably have to go through a normal door, open such a door and close it, and walk up and down stairs or over irregularities on the floor. It will not look at all like a human being, but rather like a box with one large eye at the top, two arms, three hands, and a pair of long narrow pads on each side to support and move itself with.

The problem of making the machine respond to the presence of objects in different places such as the foot of the staircase has already been solved, in partial prototypes. The chief difficulty is undoubtedly the coordination of hand and eye – for example, to teach the machine to distinguish between a knife and a fork and to lay them on opposite sides of the place at the table. However, it is true that the fundamental problem of distinguishing between objects of different shapes by a computer has already been partially solved and published, and therefore there is no basic problem in this. When one considers the immense change in the size and reliability of computers and all other electronic devices that has taken place, first in going from mechanical operation to the vacuum tube, and then to a transistor, it is clear that computers for doing this type of control of movement according to sense impressions will certainly be available before 1984.

Preliminary work on the design of suitable walking and stair-climbing mechanisms has already shown that there are no major problems in this field, and the design of arms with the necessary degrees of freedom and of hands both for picking up objects and for gripping and rotating an object indefinitely in either direction is well advanced. Storage batteries or directly fuelled cells will certainly be well enough developed to provide say 1kW for 1 hour with a weight of 20 lb. or so.

Basically, applied science starts with the clear understanding of a human need and then uses all the available scientific knowledge to assist in the achievement and satisfaction of this need. Helping the housewife by eliminating the routine operations is the outstanding human need in the developed countries that calls for solution by 1984. The only problem is whether a sufficient number of applied scientists will have recognized and decided to work for the achievement of this need and will have obtained the necessary financial backing. We can expect to see, first, the development of a robot for some purpose where money is no object, such as for rescuing people from burning houses or aeroplanes or putting out oil-well fires.

CHANGING PATTERNS OF FAMILY LIFE

by Dr Michael Young

Institute of Community Studies, Bethnal Green, London

The first and most obvious thing to say about family life is that it will not change much by 1984. The family is the only one of our social institutions that a visitor from 984 or 84 would recognize. He would be surprised to see tiny girls rolling on their tricycles around the TV idol in the corner of the room. But he would soon notice (or perhaps just take it for granted) that there were still mothers and fathers and children smiling and glaring at each other over the plates of meat. The same goes for any of us who survive till 1984. All sorts of small instruments will be shrilling away with their new tunes; but from the family ground bass we shall hear the same figure as today.

Yet, of course, there will be plenty of small changes. I will pick on one extension of what has been happening to the family for a century or more, the growing supremacy of the immediate family; and one rather new trend, the increase in the birth rate.

Supremacy of the immediate family. In almost all pre-industrial societies, including our own before the Industrial Revolution, the kinship group mattered a great deal more, and the marriage relationship a great deal less, than it does now. This was partly a matter of security. Neither husband nor wife could depend on one another for very long in a period when mortality rates were so high. Prospects for survival were better if one was firmly attached to the family into which one was born, and could bind even distant relatives into a system of mutual obligations. The oldest fit male member of the kinship group was normally its leader, with authority over the younger married people. The remnants of this arrangement can still be seen in any farming district of Britain, and in some of the family businesses which still flourish, even in electronics.

This ancient system seems to have been succeeded, for manual workers' families, by an odd version of itself. Instead of a wide-ranging kinship group – its extent depending on how far back the common ancestor was traced, from whom descent was claimed – there came an 'extended family' consisting of members of three generations who lived to some extent as a common household. The moving forces in this disposition were no longer men, but women. This new, and transitional, sort of extended family was again partly a device to increase security. Men could not be depended upon when their jobs were unsure and their wages erratic, and when they had obligations to their parents and siblings; and women had to band together if they and their children were to survive at all. The mark of this arrangement is still upon practically all 'working-class' families. Women are inclined to stick to each other, and to their women's jobs; and men to theirs, inside and outside the home. There is also a fairly strict division of family finances, and it is still common, in any but the younger couples, for the wife to know only what 'wages' her husband gives her, not what he earns.

But the trend is clear. Gradually the ties to the extended family are becoming less pressing, and the ties to the 'immediate family' (as the unit of parents and dependent children is often called) more so. Homes are more comfortable, the five-day week is established, and husbands are in the kitchen, taking an interest in domestic life which was rare even forty years ago. If men are in their concerns more like women, women are more like men. They go out to work more often and earn their own money to put alongside their husbands'. Even working-class husbands are sometimes to be seen with aprons, and wives with trousers, although it is still very unusual indeed to find a working-class wife who is allowed to drive her husband's car. By 1984 it will be more usual. There will be more of that give and take between men's and women's roles which is the practical expression of a belief in sex equality, and hence less of a gap between the styles of life of the different social classes. The 'status' of women will be still higher, and so will that of children.

What will be the consequences for old people? In the more distant past, the oldest male enjoyed a predominance, and in propertied families sometimes still does; in the working classes the oldest woman was the queen-pin of the extended family, ruling over her daughters and their children. There will be fewer paramount old people by 1984, and more loneliness. This is not to say that the three-generation household will be a thing of the past – far from it. I would expect that, as the standard of life grows, more young couples will find room in their houses for their aged parents, when they are widowed or incapable of looking after themselves. The difference from earlier times will be that the grandparents will no longer be in a position of authority; rather will they be subject to the authority of their own children. More and more, their common state may create a new bond between grandparents and grandchildren – that is, wherever the grandchildren have not succeeded the grand-parents as the rulers of the family. The adaptable house of 1984 will be one that can be adapted to contain grandparents, in their own separate apartments, whenever the need arises.

Increase in the birth rate. Demographers were caught out in the 1930s and 1940s by their forecasts of population decline, and they are now rightly cautious about their predictions. But it is becoming increasingly clear that, after a century of falling family size, there has been a turn-round in the birth rate in the United States since the Hitler War and that, at a more measured pace, Britain and other countries in Western Europe are, in this as in other things, following on. Total population threatens to rise in the more advanced industrial countries just as it does in the underdeveloped. No one yet knows the reasons for this change. Full employment, growing prosperity, and better social services have something to do with it: no longer do most couples have to worry too much about the poverty of which children used to be one of the great causes. But I would guess that the new supremacy of the immediate family, of which I have already spoken, is a more important (though by no means independent) influence. Home is becoming more absorbing, with its complex array of comforts, with the scope it offers in and out of the garden for aesthetic creativity, with its 'movable room' in the motor car; and at the same time the autonomy of the home stands in increasingly marked contrast to the lack of autonomy outside the home. The great world grows more impersonal and difficult to understand, as bureaucracy and specialization extend their hold, while the little world of home grows more intimate and cosy. Is it surprising that men and women, now taking joint decisions more effectively than ever, on conception as on other things, should decide to fill their little domain with more of the people who keep it alive and absorbing? Children make it easier than ever to turn in on the home.

Whatever the explanation, it seems at present unlikely that this new trend will be reversed before 1984. If not, it will mean that even more of our material resources will have to be devoted to housing, to building more large houses, that the same goes for schools and universities, and that the rush to the suburbs may become a rout.

Government

UNCONDITIONAL SURRENDER TO FACTS?

by Professor Asa Briggs

Dean of Social Studies, University of Sussex

There are several common twentieth-century trends in the government of most countries. Outstanding among them are an increase in governmental functions and in the number of people administering them, a collective preoccupation with economics and social purpose, and a popular personalization of politics made the more effective by modern mass media of communication.

There is no reason to believe that any of these trends will be reversed between now and 1984. Each trend, however, will reflect new tendencies. Governmental functions are likely to depend more and more on long-term assessments of the future, and the people administering them will require more of a logistic and less of a bureaucratic training and outlook. There are likely also, in relation to this first trend, to be checks and swings, with new checks being devised both in non-communist and communist countries, and with swings of opinion and control, the swings never restoring an old situation exactly as it was.

The second trend will involve governmental concern with the public implications of social and economic issues which are at present only dimly formulated, among them automation in highly developed economies and, in undeveloped or developing countries, action to develop the real constituents of economic enterprise. Disillusion with the rhetoric of economic growth is as likely to disturb new countries in the 1980s as the impact of political men on customary social structures has done in the recent past. The reaction of government to disenchantment may be politically repressive or socially adventurous: in either case it will probably emphasize even more than today the need for strong leadership. We shall not exorcise the charismatic element from government.

In 1984, the third of the twentieth-century trends, that towards political personalization, may conceal from the public even more than it does today the realities of politics and administration. New countries lean heavily on myths of individuals. Old countries in their international contacts make more and more of them. Detailed background work on long-term plans, including intelligence and research, will place great power in the hands of people relatively unknown to the public, but at the same time it will make the techniques and arts of presentation more, not less, important. Yet educational changes will increase – in all countries – the number of critical observers of the process: the main resistance to the misuse of governmental power will lie here rather than in intermediate institutions created in the past. It will not always be an adequate check – further institutional checks will have been sought and in some cases found – but government will always have to take account of it.

Yet, in 1964, behind the common trends in government there are immense divergences between the different governments, and we lack adequate typologies to sort them out. For this reason, even if the biggest issue in international politics is left on one side, our ability to avoid nuclear war, all forecasts of what will happen within domestic government or between governments are extremely hazardous. Indeed, there is likely at the same time to be both more conflict and more cooperation. The very units of government themselves are likely to be different in 1984. In Africa and Asia inherited sovereignties and frontiers are likely to be disputed through sequences of 'crises', although there are powerful nationalist tendencies to confirm flamboyantly what on social and economic grounds seems to have little *raison d'être*. By 1984 it should be clear, after protracted uncertainty, whether or not twenty-first-century Africa will follow the pattern of nineteenth-century Latin America.

In Europe – and across the Atlantic – a considerable amount of government, particularly in economic matters, constituting a far greater segment of government than now, is likely to be shared between countries. Through the politics of science, of food, and of disarmament this sharing may cut across power divisions. Yet

many of the forces making for increased sharing of government
are likely to be removed from public scrutiny, perhaps even more
if there were a long period of co-existence. For most countries,
the margin of choice in politics is likely to be still further
narrowed, less for reasons of ideology than through 'unconditional surrender to facts'. At critical points in the process of
narrowing, however, there may well be what, at least super-
ficially, will seem to be dramatic moments of decision.

The biggest divergence in government now is between 'old'
countries faced with the formidable task of adapting or radically
overhauling inherited institutions and procedures and 'new'
countries creating political complexes, including political parties
and civil services, for the first time. In both cases there is
strain, caused in the one case by too many overheads, in the other
case by too little capital. On each side, also, considerable
imaginative sympathy – even more than detailed factual knowledge – is necessary to bridge gulfs. The gulfs may have widened
and deepened by 1984.

As far as the 'old' countries are concerned, the shape of
government in 1984 will depend in the first instance on the will
to make sweeping changes in the 1960s and on the extent and
character of the social as well as the political overhaul. In the
second instance it will depend on more long-term changes in
social structure and economic achievement. In Britain, for
example, government will probably be increasingly professiona-
lized, although each particular government may rely more on
sympathetic expert assistance from outside than has been
common in the past. Mobility in and out of administration will
probably have extended from economists to other social scientists
and probably to people in labour and business. Central government will be better informed in respect of both the quantity and
quality of information, more active in seeking to encourage
enterprise and control social change, more concerned with the
long-term effects of its policies. Treasury control will have given
way to production planning, but the psychology of industrial
relations will still preoccupy the planners.

Parliament, either by decisive action or relentless cumulative
pressure, will probably have reformed many of its procedures,
and a more intelligent use will be made of parliamentary com-

mittees in matters both of economics and international politics. There will still be 'dignified' parts of the constitution, increasingly divorced, perhaps, from their public-service origins. The old ideal of public service will have been battered, and there will be a search for substitutes. The role of political parties will have been modified considerably within a framework of long-term planning, but their rhetoric may not have substantially changed. Their behaviour will be more carefully scrutinized by those 'critical observers' whose numbers will increase, but this scrutiny may in itself lead to greater demands for increased political participation. There will be no substitute in the British type of political system for free elections, although the psychology of elections is likely to create as much interest in the future as psephological statistics do today.

The 'new' countries are likely to diverge more from each other in 1984 than they do today, with the future of many of them depending on their willingness to accept ideas and policies which at the moment command only very limited assent. In some of them, at least, what at present seems to be an 'interim' pattern of government will have come to an end and, within a new economic and social framework, some of the same problems will be posed which have been posed in other parts of the world in the past. There will probably be more talk, indeed, of old problems than of new countries, with food, population, unemployment, technology, economic enterprise, and political rights, central issues of policy.

Such general forecasts presuppose avoidance of general nuclear conflict or of international economic cataclysm. They are by no means incompatible, however, with continuing outbreaks of violence or with a series of economic crises. It is difficult to go further than this because government for the most part registers change before it speeds it up or regulates it, and the positive response which is necessary before change can be accelerated is not always forthcoming. People count, both in power and out of it. Out of the experience of change, whether or not it is initiated by government, there will probably emerge new political theories, pushing beyond the frontiers of Marxist and anti-Marxist debate, some of them emerging within Marxism itself. Quite apart from the pressure of economics on government policy or the greater influence of applied psychology, these theories themselves are likely to be in universal circulation by 1984. And it will be difficult, given the communications revolution, for any government to insulate itself from them.

COMMUNICATIONS AND GOVERNMENT

by Dr V. K. Zworykin

R.C.A. Laboratories, Princeton, New Jersey

Government, to be good, must be informed; to be democratic, it must be controlled by an informed citizenry. These conditions can be realized only by an efficient system of two-way communication between the people and their governmental agents.

The problem of presenting the government's message to the people has found an adequate solution. Broadcast radio and television not only enable heads of governments to address themselves to their total constituencies at short notice, but permit minor functionaries as well to acquaint people in limited areas concerning school closings, road alterations, counter-measures for epidemics, and other matters of importance for the efficient operation of society.

By comparison, the ways open to the people for making their wishes known to their representatives appear quite inadequate. The one official channel available for this purpose is the vote. The cumbersome business of preparing and printing the ballots, setting up the polling places, and requiring voters to present themselves there at appointed times, limits both the frequency of such expressions of public opinion and the range of issues covered by them. More often than not, the election centres on a personal contest between candidates, and the issues responsible for success or failure become the subject of a guessing game for commentators, candidates, and campaign managers. The extensive use of unofficial public opinion polls is a natural consequence. Yet, these too, apart from being subject to sampling errors, are too time-consuming to give the people an effective voice in time of crisis.

This limitation on the democratic process is not at all necessary. As I have had occasion to point out in my Clerk Maxwell Memorial lecture to the British Institution of Radio Engineers (*Journal of the British I.R.E.*, Vol. 19, p. 529), modern technology makes it possible to give the people the ability to communicate their wishes and opinions to the government with a directness and immediacy comparable with that realized at present only in the opposite direction.

To be sure, doubt may be expressed as to the desirability of direct popular control of public policy. The past experience with the direct democracy of ancient Athens and the town meeting may be interpreted either favourably or unfavourably or even regarded as irrelevant, in view of the greater complexity of the questions presented to modern governments for decision. Three comments may here be in order. First, in direct democracy as in our present-day representative governments, it may be assumed that only broad policy decisions would be made by laymen and that details would be left to the judgement of a hierarchy of technical advisers. Second, being repeatedly called on to participate in public decisions can be expected to stimulate in the citizen an increased sense of responsibility and a desire to inform himself on public questions; thus the practice of direct democracy can help to develop the preconditions for its success. Finally, whatever the manner may be in which the expression of public opinion is translated into the control of public policy – and I cannot pretend to any special knowledge in this field – it would certainly be of value to those who guide the nation to have an accurate index of public attitudes on important issues. For this last reason alone we might expect that, by 1984, governments will have availed themselves of the technical possibility of accurately gauging popular response to current and projected policies.

In the technically advanced countries of today, the desired two-way communication between citizens and government is made possible by the existence of two parallel communication systems with practically complete coverage of the population – the broadcasting system and the telephone system. For example, in the United States, with 82 million telephones serving a population of some 190 million, it would be a relatively simple matter to 'assign' every voter to a particular telephone, a limited number of public telephones taking care of non-subscribers.

In the system envisaged, every telephone would be provided with simple auxiliary equipment, which would convert it into a voting station. Registered voters assigned to the station would then be in a position to express their preferences on specific questions submitted over broadcast channels at any pre-assigned voting period in much the same manner as citizens today use voting machines for expressing their opinions in a referendum. The important difference resides in the fact that such a poll could be conducted at any time, upon a few hours' notice; that the voting would be carried out predominantly at home, without delay or interference with the normal routine of the voter; and that the returns could be known within an hour after the voting had been completed. For details as to how this might be accomplished the reader is referred to my earlier paper. As indicated there, the obvious requirements that only qualified voters participate in the vote and do so only once can be met without difficulty.

Let us assume that, by the year 1984, a basic reform of this nature in the recording of public opinion has been carried into effect. What would be the consequences? First of all, government leaders would be able to align their policies more closely with the popular will, which would be known rather than a subject for speculation. In this manner they might avoid forced reversals of policy and give government a greater degree of continuity. Even more important, the frequent consultation of the individual voter on specific issues would tend to overcome his feeling of political ineffectiveness and provide him with a recurrent incentive to become better informed on matters of public policy. In this manner we may hope that, in 1984, an appropriate application of modern communication techniques may strengthen the basis of effective democratic government by creating a better informed and more vitally interested citizenry and rendering government more responsive to its will. An effective way would have been found for the citizen to communicate with his government and for the government to become aware of the popular will.

COMPUTER MODELS OF THE ECONOMY

by Professor Richard Stone

Faculty of Economics and Politics, University of Cambridge

In the last generation an important new development in economic analysis has been the construction of computable models of the economic system. There is much talk nowadays about economic models, in spite of which many people may still be wondering what an economic model actually is. It is not a parsimonious blonde or a 50 m.p.g. minicar. Nor is it a piece of mechanical or electrical apparatus. It is a set of algebraic equations intended to reflect the facts of economic life and to show how these facts are related to each other.

A very simple example of an economic model, which is not, however, without some interest, can be set out as follows:

(1) an accounting relationship which says that income (or output) equals expenditure plus saving, or $y = e + s$;

(2) another accounting relationship which says that saving equals investment, or $s = v$;

(3) a behavioural relationship which says that the community always saves a fixed proportion of its income, or $s = \pi y$, where π denotes the constant proportion of income saved; and

(4) a technical relationship which says that income (or output) increases in proportion to investment, or $v = \rho \dot{y}$, where ρ denotes the capital-output ratio, namely the number of £s' worth of capital needed to produce one £'s worth of output and $\dot{y}$ denotes the change of income over a certain period.

An economy governed by these four relationships will grow at a rate of π/ρ, which means that in order to grow faster it must either save a larger proportion of its income, that is increase π, or learn to use less capital per unit of output, that is reduce ρ. For example, if it saves 10 per cent of its income and has a capital-output ratio of 2·5, it will grow at a rate of 4 per cent; if it could either increase its saving to 12·5 per cent or lower its capital-output ratio to 2, it would grow at a rate of 5 per cent. Thus we can see what would have to be done if that economy wanted to change its rate of growth.

The four equations given above constitute a toy model, so to speak. Obviously, if an economic model is to reflect adequately the complexity of the real world, it must be much more complicated. Indeed, some of the models now in existence contain thousands of relationships, each capable of being translated into an arithmetical operation. But when it comes to putting figures in the place of letters, the calculations involved are discouragingly formidable. On the other hand, until the relationships have been checked in the light of figures, nobody can be absolutely certain of their validity. For this reason the production of economic models has until recently remained, with very few exceptions, within the confines of academic research. In the last few years, however, the enormous strides made in the development of computers have revolutionized this activity and opened up the possibility of making quantitative models which will be detailed enough and reliable enough to play an important practical role in government and business planning.

This role will consist not in telling people what they are to do, but in giving them more information on which to base their decisions. After all, an economy is nothing but a system which transforms information into decisions; so a necessary condition for its efficient functioning is that an adequate amount of information be available in the right place at the right time. A market mechanism does not automatically generate this information. Many public and private bodies try to remedy this deficiency by making special surveys, projections, etc. But just because the economy is a system, because, that is, its different parts are interdependent, the task is very difficult for any group or individual working in isolation. A central planning mechanism runs into the opposite problem: it is hopeless to try to concentrate all decisions at a single point, because sufficient information cannot be concentrated there. The result in both cases is that, too often, apparently wise decisions miscarry, well-meaning efforts are frustrated, and valuable resources, both material and intellectual, are wasted.

More and more people are recognizing these difficulties and looking to economic models as the most promising tool for overcoming them in the future. All over the world, economists, with the help of computers, are working at perfecting such models. I shall give a single example of what this kind of work entails.

GOVERNMENT

In the last four years a group of us at Cambridge has been engaged in building a computable model of the British economy. Progress reports on this work are published in the series *A Programme for Growth* (Chapman and Hall, London). We now have a working prototype which, while still much in need of improvement, shows that the task is a manageable one.

Briefly, our first endeavour has been to build up a picture of the economy in 1970 based on specific assumptions about the standard of living in 1970 and about its rate of growth thereafter. The economic consequences of these assumptions can be set out as a series of balances: (i) the balances of supply and demand for the 31 product-groups distinguished in our model; (ii) the balances of revenues and costs in the corresponding branches of production; (iii) the balance of supply and demand for labour; (iv) the balance of saving and investment; and (v) the balance of Britain's external account.

Some idea of the part played in this exercise by the computer can be gained from the following figures. The whole economy is represented by the entries in a set of 253 balancing accounts. Each account shows the incomings and outgoings of some branch or sector of the economy. The numerical inputs (parameters and conditions) needed for a computer-run number between 5000 and 6000. A run involves about 30 million multiplications: on a desk calculator this is equivalent to 60 man-years of work; on the Atlas computer it takes 22 seconds.

From this experience it seems to me legitimate to suggest that, by 1984, a computable model of the economy, covering all aspects of economic life and perhaps some aspects of social life too, will be an established part of the machinery of economic organization. This model should not be thought of as a huge single entity but as a multiple one, a system of models, in which the central model will provide no more than an outline of the whole picture and will be connected by data-links to a series of sub-models. Each sub-model will work out the details of some aspect of the whole: some branch of the productive system, say, such as the power industries or the transport network; or a social service, such as education or public health. Each sub-model will rely for its inputs partly on the output of the other models and partly on a running supply of current statistical information; for by then the country's statistical services will be entirely run on computers, and basic sources such as the census of population or the census of production, which now take months and years to compile, will be available on the ticker-tape. Finally, each sub-model will be handled by a group of people with an intimate knowledge of the activity concerned and, apart from the exchange of outputs, will be operated independently of the others; in addition to its other advantages, this arrangement will ensure that the requirements of government and business secrecy are respected.

For any chosen target, the model-system will produce a complete picture of the economy in which every detail will be in harmony with the target, whether this be set in the near or the distant future. If the finished picture, or some part of it, appears on inspection to be unacceptable, the target can be modified and the change fed back into the model-system. A new picture will then emerge, and if this is not acceptable either, the process can be repeated until a possible future that seems satisfactory is mapped out. Thus we may hope to see reconciled the advantages of individual initiative with those of central planning.

One final word. Computers do sums, men take decisions. An ability to do sums is likely to change men's opinions on what actions seem sensible; but the responsibility for these actions rests with men, not with computers.

'REPORT OF THE COUNCIL FOR SCIENCE POLICY, 1983-4'

by Dr Alexander King

Director for Scientific Affairs, Organisation for Economic Cooperation and Development, Paris

London, 1984. – The British government's Council for Science Policy devotes much of its Report for 1983–4 to consideration of the place of science in the machinery of government. That has been a recurrent theme amid the continual changes in the organization of science which have taken place ever since the Council was created (from the old Advisory Council) following publication of the Trend Report some twenty years ago. The present report is particularly interesting, however, in that it records the structural adaptation which has followed the somewhat belated entry of Britain into the European Federation.

After various unsuccessful experiments in organization, the basic concept is again that of a single Ministry of Science under a senior cabinet member. It consists of a secretariat and a colony of some twenty specialist research councils for the natural, technological, social, and human sciences. Many of these research councils, particularly where very expensive equipment is necessary, operate their own laboratories, as well as field stations in different parts of the world. Earlier criticism of these institutions has largely been met by their gradual relocation on the campuses of the new universities, and by financial and pension arrangements which allow easy transfer of staff with universities and industry. The other research councils work mainly in financing research in universities and independent institutes so as to provide solid support for outstanding workers in their particular fields, but always within a reasonable balance of effort. The resources now available for this work and the vigour of the programming methods have done much to remove the threat of creeping mediocrity which seemed to menace so many of our research schools in the decade after university financing fell to a monolithic Ministry of Education.

The whole system functions, of course, under the supervision of the Council for Science Policy itself, which exercises control on behalf of the Minister. It distributes money to the constituent specialist bodies; the overall balance of effort is continuously readjusted in the light of new discoveries of scientific importance in all parts of the world, complementary international efforts, and the changing needs of economic, social, defence, and foreign policy.

The Council is served by the Central Scientific Secretariat, responsible for providing the background data and studies required for a comprehensive science policy, as well as for maintaining day-to-day liaison with 'the Plan', with industry, and with the specialist research councils. Amongst work in progress are (1) the provision of detailed statistics of research and development expenditure, (2) advanced studies in technological forecasting, (3) special surveys of selected scientific fields and of the research needs of different sectors of the economy, (4) investigations of the relationship between scientific creativity and different types of research organization, (5) studies to elucidate more clearly the nature and economic significance of technological innovation and of the sociology of change, (6) forecasts of the impact of certain scientific developments on foreign policy, and (7) the development of electronic models of the economy and of research input-output networks.

The Secretariat consists of some 187 professionals, most of whom are natural and social scientists, economists, and operational research workers. It is difficult to see how such a small group can seriously hope to undertake the vast range of investigation and analysis required to maintain a realistic and balanced policy, and it is to be hoped that the Minister will assert his authority to prevent this work being permanently weakened by the dominance of immediate Treasury considerations.

Science and 'the Plan'. For many years, applied research and development for particular economic sectors came directly under the Minister for Economic Affairs. This separation of applied from fundamental research proved somewhat sterile, in that it encouraged a tendency for industries to miss significant innovation possibilities arising from research in fields which did not seem immediately relevant. Furthermore, quickening rates of innovation demanded not only applied research but ever-increasing efforts of suitably oriented fundamental investigation. Finally, fundamental knowledge in many fields, starting with space research, radio-astronomy, and high-energy physics, has required, for its own expensive instruments of probe, the development of new, special technologies.

In fact, the distinction between fundamental and applied research has evaporated – except in terms of objective. It is five years now since all national scientific effort has been restored to the care of a single Ministry of Science. Articulation with economic and social policy is ensured by the presence in the Secretariat of a number of economists from 'the Plan', while there is a group of scientists in the latter organization responsible for the chapters of 'the Plan' concerning research and education for science and technology.

It is interesting to note that the research chapter of the present

plan devotes just under 10 per cent of its resources to fundamental research, probably too low a figure in view of the rising
costs of equipment in expensive subjects such as interplanetary
radiation, photo-conversion, and biophysics.

Science and industry. This section of the report is mainly concerned with reviewing results of work on the function of
research in sustained economic growth. On the institutional side,
however, it should be noted that there are now only eleven
main research associations in Britain, together with some thirteen branches of federal research associations having their
headquarters in other European countries.

National, federal, and international research. The work of the
Science Policy Council has become immeasurably more complicated by the need to balance national research effort with that
supported by funds outside its direct control, coming from
federal income tax. There has been much criticism of late as to
the extent of federal research outside Britain, yet the report
quotes a balance of payments study which indicates that for every
Eurodollar contributed by the British taxpayer to the federal
budget, $1·43 is spent on federal laboratories within the United
Kingdom. The present report gives some details of the programmes of the Federal Radio Astronomy Centre at Jodrell
Bank, the new Institute of Biosociological Techniques, and also
the Station for Applied Photosynthesis in Ruanda which is
under British direction.

The trend towards international scientific effort, which began
in the 1950s, continues. The promise of scientific discovery, its
volume, and its cost are all so great that even the largest countries
are unable to undertake through their own resources more than
a fraction of the desirable investigations. As a result all nations
are forced in the direction of cost-sharing through combined
research effort. While Britain's adhesion to the European
Federation has greatly added to the strength and potential of her
research effort, the Federation is itself too small a unit for
effective work in the more expensive fields. The recent establishment of a Western Science Council between the Federation,
U.S.A., and U.S.S.R., while mainly concerned with evolving a
single work programme on space, will inevitably become involved in other subjects.

Operational research. A feature of 1983-4 has been the success of the Operational Research Course for Ministers. The scientific approach to political decision-making has for long been resisted and it is only now that the facilities of the Operational Research Centre of the Ministry of Science have been seriously used. This year's course has been attended by thirteen members of the Cabinet, many junior Ministers, and fifty M.P.s, including a member of the Shadow Cabinet. The purpose of this training is to familiarize politicians with the use of analysed data on current problems prepared by their operational research teams, and to appreciate quickly the consequences of alternative decisions as worked out by computers.

Final decision rests, as always, on individual experience and judgement, so that the political process is in fact strengthened, rather than diminished as detractors have claimed. Despite the current enthusiasm of Ministers for operational research techniques we may suspect that many years have still to pass before major political decision will give as much weight to an accurate and analysed presentation of real facts, as to subjective judgements, founded all too often on outworn concepts of a former party political nature.

Education

UNIVERSAL LITERACY IN THE AGE OF TECHNOLOGY

by René Maheu

Director-General, United Nations Educational, Scientific and Cultural Organization, Paris

It is no easy task to make a projection of even twenty years in a field that is shifting as rapidly as education is today. The factors which lead to caution are evident: education is sensitive to demographic changes, it is an intimate part of the social and economic fabric, and it depends very much on political conditions. What I am going to say rests on the postulate that recent trends – since about 1950 – will continue; and that we shall have the peace and economic progress which will enable education both to develop and to contribute in its turn to peace and prosperity.

What are the trends apparent today that will have the most effect upon education in 1984? The first is probably the ferment of political independence. Significantly, the newly created states as a whole devote the greatest proportion of their resources to education, even when other social services are lacking; the goal striven for is to generalize primary education. Next, there is the realization of the economic importance of education. This new notion has provided a powerful incentive to developed as well as underdeveloped countries to improve and extend facilities at the second and third levels of education.

A third tendency may be described as a growing effort to view educational policy on a broader basis – the integration of educational strategies. This may be seen nationally in the attempts to plan educational development for all levels in close concert with plans for economic and social development: regionally, states are grouping themselves more closely to pursue cooperative programmes; and still more widely, international programmes for assistance and understanding between countries and regions are also increasing in magnitude and scope. Finally, advances in our knowledge of the learning process and in teaching techniques (exemplified, for instance in programmed instruction, teaching machines, television films, and the language laboratory) are likely to have a marked effect during the next decade on what is taught, how it is taught, and how fast and how well it is learned – that is, on the general nature and rhythm of the educational process.

What then will the educational scene be in 1984?

Starting with the problem of illiteracy, I believe that we shall have reached the stage of universal primary schooling – a reduction from the present 40 per cent of children without any schooling at all to a figure of, say, 10 per cent or less. And harnessed to this great drive we shall also see a systematic attack on the remains of adult illiteracy, so that the present world figure of around 700 million adult illiterates will certainly be diminished. These two aspects of educational activity will be seen as parts of a whole and not, as is too often the case today, as competing for limited financial resources.

This forecast is based on the fact that the most remarkable educational achievement of the past decade has been the great extension of primary schooling in the underdeveloped regions of the world, where enrolments have increased from under 50 per cent to over 60 per cent of the child population. In a period of rapid population growth this has meant a virtual doubling of school places. A series of regional conferences held by Unesco in the past three years has shown that the countries of these regions have set their sights on full schooling by 1980. While the target is a possible one, it is likely to be reached only if the braking force of adult illiteracy is removed.

There is an urgency in the solution of the problem of illiteracy. It is increasingly recognized that the policy of providing schools, while communities as a whole remain illiterate, becomes more costly and less effective as time passes. Moreover, both political stability and the hope for economic and social progress depend on a speedy reduction of the present-day illiteracy rate among adults. Having recently taken part in regional conferences in Asia, the Arab States, and Africa, I am deeply impressed by the degree to which the developing States realize the nature of the problem and desire its solution. The question now before us is whether practical and rapid measures will result from this awareness and these aspirations. For, indeed, the future is not simply a projection of past trends, but is also the outcome of what in our time we do to shape it.

On the side of formal education, by 1984 we should have schooling – if only for 4 to 6 years – for nearly all children in the less developed areas. In the industrially developed regions, technological development will maintain the trend towards lengthening the period of compulsory education, and will probably make it necessary for all children to receive a complete secondary course – in other words, to remain at school for a period of twelve years. Some have seen in this a widening educational gap between the developed and the developing countries which may cause the latter to despair of overtaking their more favoured fellows. However, I believe that this gap, real as it may be at present, will by the 1980s have started to close – but only started, and only if the present effort is sustained.

All educational expansion carries with it the question of the supply of teachers. This brings me to the question of the teacher's training and status. At present, two opposing trends may be observed. On one hand, nearly all countries find it difficult to recruit enough able young people to the profession. The competing demands and superior rewards of other occupations, mainly technological, lie at the root of this shortage, and various short-cut remedies are being sought. At the same time, the very complexity of the teacher's task leads to proposals for lengthening the period of training and for improving the status of the profession. I hesitate to predict what the outcome in 1984 will be. But it is clear that without a serious reassessment of the teacher's role in society the quantitative extension of literacy will still be out of gear with our changing social needs.

Indeed, if we are adequately to forecast the education of the future, we have to situate it in the context of the technological revolution. The vastly increasing body of scientific knowledge and rapid changes in occupations which apply this knowledge represent what might be termed an 'exponential' challenge to the schools. There is, of course, an enduring element in education, the teacher–student relationship; but in the external trappings of teaching and learning the school seems to have changed little over the past fifty years. In responding to the challenge of technology, education itself is likely to become more technological.

Some signs of the change can already be seen. In school buildings of the future, a more flexible use will be made of space and materials, so as to allow for better setting and streaming of students and for a combination of group work with individual study. Corresponding changes may be expected in organization, with comprehensive schools more general than they are now and a better blend of academic, cultural, and practical elements in the curriculum.

Recent research on learning and the improvement of teaching aids will combine to give the future teacher and student a remarkable range of means for communicating, for drawing on knowledge and skills far beyond the classroom, and for evaluating progress.

Ultimately, technological changes in education will not only make possible a quantitative expansion but will also encourage qualitative improvements. We know that in most of the world's schools today learning is a painful rote effort, at which far more fail than succeed. Wastage rates in many countries show that less than one in five children succeed in completing the primary school course they enrol for. And, in more favoured communities, experiments with the curriculum indicate that a student can master in nine years what is traditionally taught over twelve. Such examples of wastage reveal the gap between what schooling is and what it is supposed to do. Most peoples accept as an educational goal the balance between development of the individual personality and meeting the needs of society; and the quality of education in the future should be assessed by the extent to which it succeeds in finding the balance.

On this point I believe, optimistically, that we shall make progress. The concept of permanent education is already gaining ground, and it resolves many of the apparent conflicts in our past educational thinking. There need be no opposition between general and technical education, or between science and culture, if we seek the new humanism of a scientific and industrial way of life. There should be, as the 1944 Education Act in Britain foreshadowed, no sharp cleavage between 'formal' and 'further' education. Indeed, this approach is simply a restatement of the link between school and life. And finally, life in 1984 is likely to be far more international than it is now. I expect that education at that time will reconcile national and international needs, and will see in international cooperation not only a means to, but also the goal of, educational endeavour.

GRADUATES FOR THE DEVELOPING WORLD

by Professor D. S. Kothari
Chairman, University Grants Commission, Government of India, New Delhi

Twenty years are less than the span of a generation and yet, at the pace of current developments, vast changes in the field of education are likely to occur by 1984. In some respects the scene may be totally different from what it is today. In most of the developing countries there is a massive expansion of education at all levels and a drive to eradicate illiteracy which seriously afflicts a large part of the contemporary world. According to the 1961 census in India, out of a total population of 439 million, there were only 105 million literates – 78 million males and 27 million females. The chance of a child to go to school and so not be doomed to lifelong illiteracy has been, till recently, very slender in many populous areas of the world.

By 1984, perhaps for the first time in man's history, almost every child everywhere would be at school. In India, for example, by the end of the next decade some 90 per cent of children are likely to be at school up to the age of fourteen, as compared with 23 per cent in 1961. With the rise in literacy and increasing emphasis on science education, the national productivity in developing countries is likely to improve substantially in the next two decades. There would also be a lessening of the wide gap between the developing and advanced countries in the mean expectation of life at birth.

By 1984, in many of the developing as well as advanced countries, the enrolment at the university stage is likely to ex-

pand to about two or three times the present numbers. In the
process, quality will suffer, more in some countries, less in
others, for in any large-scale expansion of education the teacher-
pupil ratio is affected adversely. Student enrolment can be
doubled in less than ten years as in India (the Robbins report
envisages a two-and-a-half-fold increase by 1980 in Britain) but
it takes much more than ten years to train and double the
number of *competent* teachers. However, if adequate care is
taken, the setback need be no more than a temporary phase.

The pattern of distribution of students amongst different
faculties – for example, the humanities, science, engineering and
technology, medicine, and agriculture – is likely to shift notice-
ably in favour of science and technology. In the U.S.A. the proportion of students in higher education studying science and
engineering has remained stationary at almost 20 per cent over
the past fifty years; and the number of science majors who move
to non-science careers is as high as 70 per cent.

In several of the developing countries, agricultural education
and research are not receiving the attention they ought to. The
effort is often below the 'critical size' to make a significant impact on food production. The proportion of university students
in agriculture in India is about the same as in Britain. It is much
more in Japan and China. The stress on agricultural education
is likely to be a dominating feature of higher education in most of
the developing countries.

A large-scale expansion of higher education is required to
meet the rapidly rising demands of industry, agriculture, and
welfare services, and other sectors of the economy. Scientists
and engineers constitute about 0·8 per cent of the total population in the U.S.A. whereas their strength is as low as 0·05 per
cent in India. According to present trends, their numbers are
likely to rise to about 1·5 per cent in the U.S.A. and to about
0·2 per cent in India by 1984. The total public expenditure on
all education, which in developing countries is generally below 3
per cent of the gross national product, will rise probably to about
5 per cent during the next two decades. It is already above 7 per
cent in the U.S.A.

It is rather a striking fact that for almost all countries the *public
expenditure on university education, expressed per student, is of the*

same order as the per capita gross national product. (This, of course, does not apply to developing countries receiving massive foreign aid for higher education.) The situation is unlikely to change in the next two decades. The current cost per university student per year is about £50 in India and £800 in the U.K., as against the per capita G.N.P. of £25 and £400 respectively. The wide gap in expenditure per student between different countries is reflected in the differing levels of educational attainment. Thus, the number of persons awarded research degrees (Ph.D. or higher) is about one per 1,000 of university students in India as compared to some ten in the U.K. In many developing countries the recurring as well as the capital spending per seat in science courses is very inadequate and very much less than it is in technology and medicine. This disparity is likely to be reduced in the years to come.

A step of considerable significance is likely to be the expansion in scope, range, and quality of correspondence courses, assisted and augmented by radio and television. A unique advantage of the correspondence courses is that their efficiency and quality tend to increase with rising enrolment. It is possible that, in the near future, under the auspices of Unesco, correspondence courses at various levels may be sponsored on an international basis, and made available to all countries for adoption or adaptation. They may bring a course of recognized content and standard within the reach of everyone.

A fundamental problem facing developing countries is how to achieve education for large numbers, and, what is still more important, education of adequate quality with relatively meagre resources. It calls for new methods and techniques, more research in education, and an ever increasing and vigorous cooperation between the advanced and developing countries.

NEW METHODS AND NEW AIMS IN TEACHING

by Professor B. F. Skinner

Psychological Laboratories, Harvard University

Improving education seldom takes the form of improving teaching. It is no doubt important to find better teachers, build more and better schools, teach less of what is not needed, bring what must be taught up to date, and reach more students through various forms of mass media. But by 1984, we should hope, teaching itself will also have been improved. The experimental analysis of behaviour, human and animal, has uncovered facts about learning and teaching which were not available when current methods were devised and which should make it possible to improve education in the plain sense of teaching more in the same time with the same effort. As a result more students should be taught, and each should be taught more and taught it more thoroughly. Each student should have a greater choice of programmes and should be able to pursue any one of them more successfully.

Some gain in this direction will come from a further abandonment of coercive techniques. The cane has in most quarters been discarded, but teachers still use less obvious forms of punishment, and – whether we like to admit it or not – most students still study mainly to avoid the consequences of not studying. Even at the university level, the commonest pattern is 'assign and test', in which the student is held responsible for learning simply in the sense that he will suffer certain unhappy consequences if he fails. In this system it is never the teacher who fails, nor can it be, for 'assigning and testing' is not really teaching at all.

It is not enough, however, simply to abandon coercive practices. The methods of Summerhill are therapeutic rather than educational. Nor will it suffice to replace punitive methods by 'enriching' our schools with real life or by turning from textbooks to non-verbal audio-visual media. There is good reason to make what is to be learned as attractive as possible, but in doing so we often deprive the student of the chance to *discover* that something is interesting when looked into. Brightly coloured illustrations in a reading primer may attract the pupil to the text they accompany, but they entertain the pupil *before* he reads; a page of black-and-white text offers him a much greater opportunity to enjoy the *consequences* of reading. The audio-visual aids of 1984 will be less concerned with attracting and holding attention.

The consequences of behaviour are particularly emphasized in the study of what is technically called 'operant conditioning'. Behaviour reinforced by its consequences is not to be confused with the conditioned reflexes of Pavlov, and only certain instances of operant reinforcement are appropriately called rewards. What is important here is the extraordinary power – fully demonstrated both in the laboratory and in field applications – to change behaviour in specified ways through properly arranged reinforcements. Students are only slightly affected by what they get out of their education in the long run. It is the immediate consequences of their behaviour which must be carefully examined and altered. Unfortunately, we cannot do this simply by applying some general principle of reinforcement, just as we cannot build bridges simply by applying general principles of stress and strain. The teacher must become a specialist in a rapidly developing scientific analysis of human behaviour.

The conspicuous signs of the new technology of teaching in 1984 will probably be the 'teaching machines' used to arrange the necessary contingencies of reinforcement. It will be easy to confuse the technology with the equipment. But machines are inevitable. Only with the help of appropriate capital equipment can teachers cope with the problems imposed on them by the extraordinary cultural changes and the growth in populations characteristic of the twentieth century.

Although the word 'machine' suggests regimentation, such devices are designed precisely to help the individual student. Students were once taught one at a time, and the ideal of individualized instruction is still preserved in statements of educational policy, but the practice has long since succumbed to the exigencies of teaching large classes. Groups of students move forward at a standard pace. Those who could move quickly are held back and grow bored; those who work slowly are pulled forward beyond their speed, finding their work more and more difficult, until they eventually give up. But speed of learning, like speed of reading, has no very important relation to the ultimate quality of the student's work. The system has often been criticized, but an effective attack upon it has at last come from the effort to arrange the contingencies of reinforcement recommended by an experimental analysis. By 1984 the fast worker will perhaps be permitted to enjoy his natural advantage, while the slow student will be able to demonstrate that he is capable of comparable achievements given enough time.

Another result of applying recent discoveries concerning learning and teaching has been a reconsideration of the 'terminal behaviours' which compose the goals of education. Just what changes in the student is the teacher to bring about? Current specifications are surprisingly vague. A related result has been the construction of sequences of responses leading to the terminal behaviours thus specified, as the student moves from ignorance to competence. Such sequences are now commonly called programmed instruction. The principle is not yet well understood, and poorly designed programmes flood the market, but by 1984 the market place should have had its well-known effect. Excellent programmes – better than any now available if the art and science of programming continue to improve – should be available in a wide range of subjects.

Many of the subjects may be unrecognizable, however. It has often been remarked that an educated man has probably forgotten most of the facts he acquired in school and university. Education is what survives when what has been learned has been forgotten. We teach 'subjects' partly because teachers are hired as subject-matter specialists and partly because competence in a given subject is convenient proof of successful teaching. But we may eventually learn how to teach the things which comprise the important marks of an education. The specific intellectual skills, abilities, attitudes, and tastes which are now taught mainly as by-products of content instruction may, if the experimental analysis of behaviour is fully exploited, occupy the focus of attention in 1984.

There will be teachers in 1984. They will not be, as they now are, doing things which can be done by machines, but with the help of machines they will be teaching effectively. Because they will have more to offer society, both their morale and their economic status will be improved. They will have the satisfaction of knowing that they are important as people.

LEARNING ALL OUR LIVES

by Lord Bowden

Principal, Manchester College of Science and Technology

It is more than fifty years since H. G. Wells told us that the whole world was engaged in a race between education and catastrophe. It is as true today as it ever was that unless all men and women have been properly educated so that they can exploit all of the best of all their talents neither the individuals themselves nor their country as a whole will ever be able to achieve a decent standard of living or take their proper place in the modern world in the second half of the twentieth century. People ought to enjoy both their work and their leisure, and education should help to fit them for both.

The problems of education have been very much in the mind of the public for years. For us in Britain, Crowther, Newsom, and Robbins have all explained why we shall have to spend a much larger part of our national income on education in 1984 than we do today. If all goes well, the last of our decaying slum schools will have been replaced by then, but I am afraid that many classes, particularly in the primary schools, will still be much bigger than they should be. Education makes great demands on our resources of man- and woman-power. Young women teachers seem to leave school to get married almost as soon as they are qualified; the birth rate is rising fast; and whatever we do it is going to be extremely difficult to provide enough teachers for all the children who must meet them face to face. We shall need all the help we can get from part-time teachers and probably from 'teachers' aides'.

Our universities will undoubtedly be much bigger in 1984 than they are today. Perhaps by then an English child will have a better chance to go to university than a Canadian has now, though we can scarcely expect that Britain will be doing as well for her young people, even then, as the Americans and the Russians do today. One young person in three in these great countries is in some type of university institution. Only one in twelve of British youngsters is as fortunate. We shall never get our problems into proper perspective unless we realize that, although American and Russian universities are already very much bigger than ours, they are still growing much faster than ours. In 1963 the budget of M.I.T. was comparable to the combined budgets of all English universities put together. There are several graduate schools in America which are much bigger than M.I.T. and they are all expanding fast. It is in these great post-graduate schools that university graduates learn to become scientists and engineers.

I hope that in twenty years' time we shall have many types of university, and that in England we shall have abandoned the attempt to conform to a pattern which was derived from the traditions of nineteenth-century Oxford and Cambridge. The Russians have developed specialized universities in some of their big factories and in their research stations, much as we have medical schools in our teaching hospitals. They may indeed be very specialized but they seem to be very useful and effective. All Soviet and American universities and many on the continent of Europe expect to play a part in the development of the whole society, and the ties between the world of scholarship, the world of industry, and the world of government are strong, complex, and all-important.

I think that the most important change in the educational system will come from a general realization during the next twenty years that education must not finish when a man leaves his school or university but that it should continue for the rest of his life. This is as true of professional men as it is of the workmen in our factories. We are rapidly and radically transforming our industries. Unskilled work is being done by machines and the work which the men have to do needs more skill and is in every way more rewarding than the routine work which machines now do and men used to do. All our people must have opportunities to re-educate themselves so that they can take their proper place in the industrial world of tomorrow. Unless we make provision on an enormous scale, and very quickly, we may have a couple of million unskilled and unemployable men, and lack as many skilled men, long before 1984.

We simply cannot tolerate such human waste and such industrial inefficiency. Every member of the working population, from managers to office boys, must gain and not lose from the new machines which are transforming our factories. We shall probably need fewer productive workers than we have today, and more people will earn their living by giving personal services to their fellow men, but everyone will need more and better training in their youth and will need retraining more than once in middle age. The total amount of scientific knowledge that we have at our disposal doubles every ten years or so. All scientists expect that they will always be more or less out of date however hard they try to keep up, but in some countries, and particularly in the U.S.A., they have long since accepted the importance of refresher courses which, for example, provide more students for M.I.T. in vacations than there are undergraduates in term time. Potential managers may come to a university for courses for a year when they are thirty or thirty-five and come again ten years later. Let us hope that the new business schools which are now being founded in England will be as successful as the business schools of America are today.

The organization of courses to re-educate and retrain people throughout their working lives will be difficult and complex. Its very unfamiliarity in Britain makes it hard for us to appreciate its importance, but adult retraining has already been developed on a very large scale in some foreign countries. The Swedes, for example, are retraining people on a scale twenty times as great as we have in Britain and both the Americans and Russians are already making most strenuous efforts to provide working men with opportunities in middle life such as they never had in their youth. Any Russian worker who is accepted for a special correspondence course and satisfies his teachers is by law entitled to forty days' free time on full pay, during which he can go to university, use the libraries and the laboratories, and meet his tutors. Other countries, too, will have to develop such schemes during the next few years. They will affect the managers, the foremen, the process workers, and the craftsmen.

The crafts unions now assume that a man learns all he needs to know during his apprenticeship before he is twenty-one. Adult re-education will obviously affect the whole structure of the trade-union movement as much as it affects the structure of the industries in which the union members work. Let us hope that, by 1984, the entire working population will be able to achieve positions, in or out of industry, which are suited to the talents of the individuals. Every man should feel that he can contribute to the welfare of his country, that he has had his chance in life and that he has made the most of it.

Cities

STABILITY AND STRIFE

by Ruth Glass

Director of Research, Centre for Urban Studies, University College, London

The future of cities has for long been a subject for utopias; and it will still be that twenty years hence. The very death of cities was, and is, one type of utopia; their transformation into neo-urban or anti-urban patterns is another. And the same kinds of design, shapely or shapeless, are drawn up at different stages of technology as 'containers' of very different projected political systems – hierarchical or egalitarian. Indeed, such utopias often serve as substitutes for political philosophy and action.

Once again, as indicated on several occasions in this series, it would be tempting to imagine a transfiguration of the cities of the world by 1984 (on the assumption that there will be a world). The stage is set for urban expansion beyond limits hitherto experienced.

Despite all the qualifications with which national population projections, and especially local projections, have to be interpreted, there is no doubt that the population of many countries – in the Americas, Asia, and Africa – is growing at a remarkable pace, and will continue to do so for some time. And this is largely happening in countries which have started on the course of industrialization, and which will have to accelerate this process. Thus people will increasingly be both 'pushed' and 'pulled' into urban areas.

By 1984, there may well be several giant urban conurbations in the world which will make the present Greater Tokyo, New York, and London look rather puny. Although some of the relevant projections are intended to be strictly hypothetical, they do show that our yardstick of measurements will have to be substantially revised. It is unlikely, for example, that Calcutta will in fact have a population of between 36 and 66 million in the year 2000 (or about 24 to 41 million in 1984) – if only because so vast an urban agglomeration could not be regarded as a single entity. Nevertheless – as Kingsley Davis, who made these projections, pointed out – while the absolute size of such a future conurbation is so far unprecedented, its proportionate size, in relation to the country's total population, would be quite modest, even by current standards. A Greater Calcutta of 66 million would, on his estimates, contain under 7 per cent of India's possible total population of one billion in the year 2000 – a smaller share of the national total than many principal cities have now. Such calculations, though not to be taken literally, indicate the contours of potential developments. The general trend is one of cumulative urban growth – the continued expansion (in terms of population, of area, or of both) of cities which are already large, in contemporary terms, rather than the multiplication of smaller urban settlements.

However, this trend, though universal in some respects, is subject to contrary influences of poverty and affluence, and takes diverse forms. In the 'developing' countries, it is generally urban growth rather than urbanization – the absolute rather than the proportionate increase of the urban population – which is proceeding rapidly, and is likely to continue. In the 'developed' countries, it is primarily not urbanization, but a process of urban diffusion – the fanning out of the urban population, and of urban occupations and culture – which is taking place. It can be expected that such diffusion will be further promoted by technological advances; and that it will still be complicated by their uneven applications. It is also evident that the ever closer liaison of men with machines, however precarious, will demand a revision of our ideas on environmental design.

Changes which have already occurred, or which are in sight – in modes of transport, in telecommunications, in automation, in building methods – could all significantly alter the organization and distribution of industries, the structure of societies and their culture, and thus also their settlement patterns. Two extreme types of pattern (each with several variants) are beginning to be envisaged – the 'elevator city', more nucleated than any previous model; and by contrast the linear series of habitations, which would hardly show the conventional distinctions between settlements, or that between town and country.

No doubt, there are vistas of great innovations. And yet I am sceptical. Although I can only express a very limited view, I take the risk of urging caution. Neither great promises nor grave warnings appear to be justified. Twenty years is a short time in the life of cities – especially on the global scale. Cities are makers of history; but they are also essentially creatures of history. Just because they often contain powerful levers of social change, they also demonstrate the long delay in the reaction of social institutions to scientific and technological opportunities. Can we expect that such time lags will become much shorter, and that governments will become rational, in the near future? Unless we do – and this would be a rash assumption – we cannot expect a radical transformation of cities by 1984.

That is not to say that there will be no new prototypes of cities. We can anticipate that some of these – new in political and physical design – will be developed in several parts of the world. But we cannot expect that the familiar urban patterns will by and large have ceased to exist; or that the city itself will have become an antiquarian type of settlement.

In many respects the structure and functions of cities have remained remarkably stable over several thousand years of recorded history. The urban infrastructure itself has conservative characteristics, for it represents not only economic, but also cultural and thus emotional investment. The very complexity of social motivation and organization is built into, and perpetuated by, the fabric of cities. And it is that complexity which determines the uses of rational capacity.

Thus cities are hardly ever modelled, or entirely remodelled, to catch up with contemporary conditions and trends. Instead, they adapt themselves slowly to such conditions, and shape the trends in their own image. We must expect that even during the next two 'development decades' societies will only rarely have the space and other resources required to reconstruct or build settlements on the scale, with the speed and pattern, commensurate to an expanding and a shifting population. Nor can it be anticipated that in general local interests will be subordinated to international priorities, determined by a global assessment of needs. Hence, by and large, the changes which will occur are still liable to be fragmentary, incoherent, even contradictory.

It is the resulting incongruities – or rather the growing awareness of such incongruities – which may well be the most striking feature of cities during the next twenty years. Never before has the juxtaposition between the 'non-contemporary' and the 'contemporary' been so inescapable everywhere, especially in cities where different phases of history have so uneasy a co-existence. You can already go on a time-travel tour in any capital of the world, and you will have many companions. Never before have the dispossessed been able to look both backward and forward so clearly, and felt so acutely that they are left behind by others who live nearby in the same calendar year. How long will Harlem remain outwardly patient with mid-town Manhattan? And this is only one of the future urban trouble spots which can be identified. There will be turmoil in and around many cities of the world even before 1984.

As the historical element in stratification has become closely enmeshed, or even coincident, with social, ethnic, racial, and territorial stratification – within nations and on the world scene – it sharpens all the other cleavages. Such socio-historical divisions will be increasingly visible in comparing cities of rich and poor nations, and also within cities, not least in those of developing countries where already old problems of poverty and new problems of affluence tend to reinforce one another.

It is the prospect of such developments which appears to be significant, much more than that of any novel blueprints of civic design. Twenty years hence the world – probably still divided into poor and rich nations, and struggling for new concepts of existence – will still have to be preoccupied with achieving the distribution of basic necessities. Except in some experimental cases, it will hardly be ready for a cross-national series of sophisticated technological 'package deals' which might produce brand new forms of habitat. And this is not wholly regrettable. We know far too little as yet about the cumulative effects of specific technical innovations, or about the dislocation and obstruction which can be caused in the initial stages of their use. Our knowledge of 'social ecology' in that sense is still very primitive. Perhaps by 1984 we shall have learned to write a programme for a computer that can provide some of the answers.

Meanwhile, when we look ahead, it is clear that the modifications of cities as artifacts will be far less important than the accentuation of their essential economic, political, and ceremonial functions. Cities can thus also be expected to retain their individuality and their capacity for self-expression. In some respects, 1984 may not be so remote from 1789 or 1917.

MULTIPLE CHOICES

by Martin Meyerson
Dean, College of Environmental Design, University of California
and Margy Meyerson
formerly Research Director, American Society of Planning Officials

The cities of 1984 can be built now. Indeed, in large measure, they are being built and have already been built, for most of what exists will survive another twenty years, barring a catastrophic war. We mean, of course, that there is enough unutilized technology and enough prototype technology to revolutionize the size, the function, the arrangement, and the appearance of cities, if enough resources were devoted to such purposes. It is even possible for the first time to by-pass the historic city and to achieve (or sustain) industrialization through patterns of development so different from the present ones that they may be regarded as 'non-urban'.

The gap between technological possibilities and technological achievement is not, of course, unique to city development. On the one hand there is a great deal of resistance to large-scale innovation, and on the other hand, there is a great deal of participation in creeping change. The failure of planned decentralization and the overwhelming spread of metropolitanization are illustrations. Nowhere in the world has government been able to carry out major programmes of redistribution of the population and of economic enterprises despite the use of stringent sanctions. Nor has any government of a developed country been able to halt the post-war suburbanization or 'scatteration' of industry, retail trade, and residences. The present urban pattern is the result of the interplay of many forces, including the mechanization of agriculture (which permitted many more people to live in cities), the shift from rail to motorized transport (which made many parcels of land in a metropolitan area equally accessible), the change in the structure of industry (which required larger land allotments and fewer workers per unit of production), the rationalization of retail trade (which produced scale economies in supermarkets and regional shopping centres and not just in central business districts). These forces, together with the baby boom, higher incomes, and changed consumer tastes have markedly altered during the past twenty years the circulation, the density, and the land use of the urban community.

These changes did not come about because of the mere knowledge of better or cheaper ways of building or of controlling the environment. The city is a dependent variable; its future physical form, like its past form, will be a response to the particular mix of human desires and economic pressures which operate nationally and locally. Thus, we foresee multiple choices rather than a single direction for the cities of 1984: for example, between centralization or decentralization of urban units and between collective or individual facilities for leisure time.

Transportation, as an illustration, can reinforce centralization or decentralization. Moving sidewalks, the monorail, the hovercraft – all are feasible means of transportation. The hovercraft potentially might have the greatest impact on urban areas. Since it moves on air cushions instead of rubber wheels, it could free people from the paved road just as they were liberated at an earlier time from the fixed rail. By traversing all kinds of terrain it could open up to development vast areas now inaccessible. Will it be used for mass transportation or for individual transportation? Will it be used to spread people more loosely through miles of urbanized development or will it be used instead to maintain the density of existing cities by making escape from the cities into the rural retreat more possible? Will those who wish to preserve a highly concentrated downtown district on a small land base, park the hovercraft on the outskirts of the central business district, or will those who wish a dispersed downtown, group buildings with surrounding hovercraft-parking compounds?

How attractive will the centres of cities be, and to whom ? Now that much of industry and wholesale and retail trade (in the United States and increasingly in Britain) has removed itself from the very centre, and now that some office functions are leaving, will closed circuit television and the walkie-talkie and other forms of communication be used so extensively that the need for face-to-face contact is further reduced ? Will airports be the locus of new centres for entertainment, restaurants, clubs, recreation, wholesaling, and professional services as more and more meetings and other activities of executives are held there ? They have already become such centres in several American cities.

What will happen to the centres of cities when more and more unskilled and semi-skilled jobs are taken over by machines ? The possibilities of further automation of continuous-flow processes, of further computerizing of billing and record-keeping, and of other kinds of mechanization raise questions not only about the location of these activities – on the outskirts of metropolitan communities or even in rural areas – but also about the work-force. Will the population be freed for more education, more skilled service and professional activity, more leisure, more creative enjoyment ? Or will people be so freed from the discipline and dignity of earning a livelihood that they become alienated from the world of increasing technology and turn to anti-social behaviour ? The former reaction would call for using the city increasingly as an educational, cultural, and entertainment apparatus. We are not sure about the implications of the latter – might there be a city specially adapted to the teenage gangs, for example ?

What happens when prefabricated (even portable) buildings and utility systems are so economical to erect that the buildings of the past and present are anachronistic ? Will this mean that the heritage of existing structures will be destroyed or revered ? Will our cities be of such unstable form that there will be neighbourhood rotation similar to crop rotation ?

What happens when more and more environmental control is possible – when snow can be melted before it sticks to the ground, when an air-conditioning shed can be erected over the entire community, when irrigation can temper the landscape and bulldozers can make hills and even mountains on a former flat plain ?

Will this stop the migration of people to the areas of most natural amenity and of pleasantest climate, and help to equalize population distribution throughout a country or the world?

These are questions which would seem, at first glance, to be more appropriate to the developed nations than the developing nations. And yet, in a sense, they are not. Technology has always permitted the developing nations to leap-frog some urban history. However, whether the cities of 1984 are to be a delight in either the developed or the developing countries will depend more on political, economic, and social than on technological changes.

Leisure and the Arts

HOW MUCH MORE LEISURE IN 1984?

by David A. Morse

Director-General of the International Labour Office, Geneva

How much leisure are we likely to enjoy in 1984? This cannot be exclusively a matter for scientific forecasting since present data on trends as well as information on the political means through which the world will seek to achieve some major social objectives are still clearly inadequate.

However, a principal element in the answer will depend upon the rate of growth in each country's productive potential per head – and how its people choose to use it. What has been past experience in these matters? Table 1 below shows the average annual rates of growth per cent in five countries. Three of them – and Italy, which is not included in the table – show remarkably rapid growth in the 1950s. These rates, though helped by the existence of under-utilized capacity and labour, augur well for the future. In the United Kingdom, where growth was not particularly fast, real income per head increased about threefold between 1860 and 1960; an annual growth rate of 4 per cent in gross national product (G.N.P.) is considered feasible.

Table 1
Real national product per head

	1860–1913	1913–38	1938–50	1950–60
France	0·9	0·9	0·0	3·3
Germany*	2·0	0·7	0·7	6·1
Japan	3·1	3·7	−3·9	7·2
UK	1·5	0·8	1·2	2·1
USA	2·3	0·9	4·2	1·1

* Federal Republic since Second World War

Many Western countries plan or envisage increases in their G.N.P. of 4–5 per cent per annum or more. Statistics from the

U.S.S.R. and other centrally planned economies, too, show increases in the national product, and they also plan for rapid growth. Allowing for population growth, sustained increases in *per capita* incomes of about 3 per cent per annum may not be beyond the powers of many countries. Increasing at 3 per cent compound interest, a figure increases by 80 per cent in twenty years and is multiplied nearly twentyfold in 100 years.

But to sustain such a rate of growth, people may have to become ever more inventive. Increasing investment in research and development and the spread of automation will help to speed growth in the future, provided countries adopt the right kind of monetary and fiscal policies, and measures to help people find, train for, and move to new jobs. On the other hand, many services seem much less amenable to automation than the production of goods, and an increase in the proportion of the labour force engaged in 'non-automatable' services will tend to slow down growth rates.

Most of the less-developed countries, as is well known, have slower rates of economic growth and much more rapid increases in population. All the signs point to a widening gap between living standards in rich and poor countries, unless economic growth in the latter can be greatly speeded up and population growth slowed down. While workers in steady jobs work long hours in some of these countries, there is in most of them a vast amount of underemployment. This is unwanted, undesirable leisure which development plans and policies seek to reduce. The next twenty years are likely to see, however, some increase in leisure for those in full-time employment in the modern sectors of these developing economies.

If the rich countries are able to increase their productive potential per head by 50–100 per cent in the next twenty years, will people wish to take out a substantial part of this increased potential in the form of more leisure? Here again past experience has been erratic and is no reliable guide to the future. Moreover, to assess past experience we should need, but do not have, statistics not only of hours worked per week but of weeks per year and years per working life. Weekly hours of work fell considerably between 1900 and 1950 (in the United States, for example, from 53 to 40), falling most in times of depression.

Since 1950 there has been on the whole rather little change in hours actually worked per week. Greater leisure has taken the form more largely of longer paid holidays, which have increased in, among other countries, France, the Federal Republic of Germany, the Netherlands, Scandinavia, the United Kingdom, and the United States. The pressures for shorter hours seem greatest at times when jobs are scarce.

Given successful employment policies in the next twenty years, a conservative forecast would be that 4–5 weeks' paid holidays per year will be common for manual workers and others, accompanied by further reductions of the order of 3–5 hours in weekly working hours. And several factors suggest that the forecast should be conservative.

First, in the next twenty years many countries may have to devote vast amounts of labour as well as of money to rebuild cities and roads.

Secondly, there is the need for increased aid to developing countries – though it may be difficult to organize this, or for developing countries to absorb it, on a scale that would make much difference to the amount of leisure enjoyed in rich countries. And I am hopeful that the world community will be willing to do much more towards bridging the gap in living standards between advanced and developing countries.

Thirdly, there is the need for more education and training. The increased pace of technical change means that people can no longer count on being able to earn their living at the same occupation all their lives. They will need to be trained for new jobs while they are still in their old ones. Within twenty years most people may expect to spend some hours a week training or retraining to keep pace with technical progress and the advance of knowledge. We should not think of this time spent learning or relearning as leisure time.

Thus, while there will almost certainly be rather more leisure in 1984, it may be not until some time later that most people will have *much* more leisure.

There is barely space to touch on the question what form the extra leisure may take. The first essential is to make sure that it does not take the form of unemployment. The second essential is that leisure should have a positive aim and not just be a negative way of filling the hours. A time may come when all our collective, as well as our individual, needs and wants may be capable of being satisfied with much less work than would provide full-time employment for the whole population available for work. Countries will then be able to choose between providing part-time work for everybody with ever fewer hours of work per year, or giving people the choice between working and not working, with adequate incomes in either case. A separation of incomes from work has already begun. There are old-age pensions, family allowances, unemployment compensation, and increasing ownership of property (investments as well as houses) by working people. Present growth rates in rich countries would make it possible before many more years to offer to everybody an adequate pension with the option of working for a supplementary income, the levels of pensions and wages being so adjusted as to attract into the labour force as many people as there were jobs for but no more. I doubt that we shall reach by 1984 the end of the curse pronounced upon Adam. But many people now alive may live to see it – or to make more accurate forecasts about it.

ATROPHIED MUSCLES AND EMPTY ART

by Sir Herbert Read

What do we mean by leisure, and why should we assume that it represents a problem to be solved by the arts? The great ages of art were not conspicuous for their leisure – at least, art was not an activity associated with leisure. It was a craft like any other, concerned with the making of necessary things. Leisure, in the present meaning of the word, did not exist. Leisure, before the Industrial Revolution, meant no more than 'time' or 'opportunity', 'If your leisure serv'd, I would speak with you', says one of Shakespeare's characters. Phrases which we still use, such as 'at your leisure', preserve this original meaning.

But when we speak of leisure nowadays, we are not thinking of securing time or opportunity to do something; time is heavy on our hands, and the problem is how to fill it. Leisure no longer signifies a space with some difficulty secured against the pressure of events: rather it is a pervasive emptiness for which we must invent occupations. Leisure is a vacuum, a desperate state of vacancy – a vacancy of mind and body. It has been commandeered by the sociologists and the psychologists: it is a problem.

Our diurnal existence is divided into two phases, as distinct as day and night. We call them *work* and *play*. We work so many hours a day, and, when we have allowed the necessary minimum for such activities as eating and shopping, the rest we spend in various activities which are known as *recreations*, an elegant word which disguises the fact that we usually do not even play in our hours of leisure, but spend them in various forms of passive enjoyment or *entertainment* – not football but watching football matches; not acting, but theatre-going; not walking, but riding in a motor coach.

We need to make, therefore, a hard-and-fast distinction *not only* between work and play but, equally, between active play and passive entertainment. It is, I suppose, the decline of active play – of amateur sport – and the enormous growth of purely receptive entertainment which has given rise to a sociological interest in the problem. If the greater part of the population, instead of indulging in sport, spend their hours of leisure 'viewing' television programmes, there will inevitably be a decline in health and physique. And, in addition, there will be a psychological problem, for we have yet to trace the mental and moral consequences of a prolonged diet of sentimental or sensational spectacles on the screen. There is, if we are optimistic, the possibility that the diet is too thin and unnourishing to have much permanent effect on anybody. Nine films out of ten seem to leave absolutely no impression on the mind or imagination of those who see them: few people can give a coherent account of the film they saw the week before last, and at longer intervals they must rely on the management to see that they do not sit through the same film twice.

We have to live art if we would be affected by art. We have to paint rather than look at paintings, to play instruments rather than go to concerts, to dance and sing and act ourselves, engaging all our senses in the ritual and discipline of the arts. Then something may begin to happen to us: to work upon our bodies and our souls.

It is only when entertainment is active, participated in, practised, that it can properly be called *play*, and as such it is a natural use of leisure. In that sense play stands in contrast to *work*, and is usually regarded as an activity that alternates with work. It is there that the final and most fundamental error enters into our conception of daily life.

Work itself is not a single concept. We say quite generally that we work in order to make a living: to earn, that is to say, sufficient tokens which we can exchange for food and shelter and all the other needs of our existence. But some of us work physically, tilling the land, minding the machines, digging the coal; others work mentally, keeping accounts, inventing machines, teaching and preaching, managing and governing. There does not seem to be any factor common to all these diverse occupations, except that they consume our time, and leave us little leisure.

We may next observe that one man's profession or work is often another man's recreation or play. The merchant at the week-end becomes a hunter (he has not yet taken to mining); the clerk becomes a gardener; the machine-tender becomes a breeder of bull-terriers. There is, of course, a sound instinct behind such transformations. The body and mind are unconsciously seeking compensation – muscular coordination, mental integration. But in many cases a dissociation is set up and the individual leads a double life – one half Jekyll, the other half Hyde. There is a profound moral behind that story of Stevenson's, for the compensation which a disintegrated personality may seek will often be of an anti-social nature. The Nazi party, for example, in its early days was largely recruited from the bored – not so much from the unemployed as from the street-corner society of listless hooligans.

Scientific studies have been made of street-corner society, out of which crime, gangsterdom, and fascism inevitably develop. It is a society with leisure – that is to say, spare time – and without compensatory occupation. It does not need a Satan to find mischief for such idle hands to do. They will spontaneously itch to do something: muscles have a life of their own unless they are trained to purposeful actions. Actions, or rather *activities*, are the obvious reflex to leisure; they consume it, and leave the problem solved.

But work is also activity, and if we reach the conclusion that all our time must be filled with one activity or another, the distinction between work and play becomes rather meaningless, and what we mean by play is merely a change of occupation. We pass from one form of activity to another: one we call work, and for that we receive pay; the other we call play, and for that we receive no pay – on the contrary, we probably pay a subscription.

No doubt it is foolish to imagine that these tendencies can change before 1984. What is more likely is that passive entertainment will fill ever-expanding periods of non-employment. Bigger and better stadia will be built to accommodate vaster and vaster crowds of football fans. Cinemas will have disappeared because it requires less effort to view the same kind of programme on the television screen. But driven out by boredom and satiation the younger people will crowd into dives where they can expend their unused energies in dancing like dervishes to the jazz bands. Another form of excitement will find its outlet in betting shops, which will have proliferated in every city, in every street. By 1984 gambling will have been nationalized and will be the greatest single source of revenue.

Meanwhile, the arts, in any historical meaning of the word, will have disappeared. Already in 1964 few people read books for pleasure; they 'use' them, or even 'view' them (books will have more and more pictures and less and less text). Poetry, already an arcane activity, will have totally disappeared. Fiction, even now a dwindling form of entertainment, will fade out and the only writers will be script-writers for the television screen. Style, in any of the arts, will be regarded as an anachronism, like ornament in architecture. The stage may still exist as a training-ground for actors, but no poets will write for it; plays will be produced by involving the actors in 'situations', for which they must improvise 'solutions'. The lighter forms of opera will survive because they are entertaining but composers like Beethoven, Wagner, and Stravinsky will be forgotten.

It is doubtful if the graphic arts will survive the present phase of action-painting. Their practice involves skill, and skill is not easily acquired. Already the art schools have abandoned any pretence to teach, and even the passive enjoyment of art, as the picture-dealers know, is beginning to decline. It is not a cheerful prospect for the arts, though there will be more and more artists in the sense of the word used by the entertainment industry. It will be a gay world. There will be lights everywhere except in the mind of man, and the fall of the last civilization will not be heard above the incessant din.

GADGETS, GAMES, AND GAMBLES

by Dr H. M. Finniston

International Research and Development Company, Newcastle-upon-Tyne

In the context of this article 'leisure' is defined as man's activities outside those in which he engages for his livelihood; the particular range of activities considered here is confined to those influenced by technology, the arts being dealt with in other contributions.

In contrast with the technological changes which will significantly affect industry and the professions, I see no corresponding revolutionary changes in the leisure practices of the various classes of society. Technology will spill over into leisure activities and tend to improve their 'mechanical' features but will not radically change the practices. This is because the present psychological approach to leisure will be the same for the next generation as it is for today's – an escape from the physical or mental concentration of work or from its responsibilities; this escapism will come either from 'spectating' or through active participation in a leisure pursuit, preferably with features contrasting with work. For the large mass of the population, it is unlikely that in 1984 the creative use of leisure in its own right will be felt as a major social justification for living (as opposed to conditioning for working); and this notwithstanding the reduced working week (which will actually obtain in practice only for certain classes), improved standards of living, and increased education.

In the home. What technological changes are likely to affect leisure in 1984? In the home, television, radio, and the gramophone (in which is included the tape recorder) will provide the principal sources of entertainment. Besides their intrinsic attractiveness to two of the major senses (sight and hearing) these products of technology have the additional merit of space-compactness, an important feature of home leisure in a society practising economic housing of population. It would not be surprising if television and radio were 'piped in' to become part of the established furnishing of the home in much the same way as the bath, the toilet, and the sink are now standard pieces of domestic equipment. Colour television will undoubtedly be con-sidered normal. The range of programmes will be extended not only through extra channels but also by borrowing on the grand scale from networked links throughout the world, directly through satellite or cable, or through recordings.

The use of television, radio, and the gramophone for education in general (including language teaching) will extend and auto-matic home-recording of television or radio programmes for play-back at convenience will increase. Whether programmed, self-adaptive teaching machines will have been developed sufficiently or cheaply enough (to buy or rent) to become part of the means for home education is uncertain.

The book will continue to be the main medium for intellectual exercise. In its physical form the book will be less permanent, increasing knowledge and subject fashion dictating rapid re-vision of paperback editions. To achieve further economies, new forms of cheap type-setting, perhaps phototype-setting, will replace present-day linotype. Newspapers will continue to be delivered through the letter-box and not printed directly to the home. Colour in newspaper will be commonplace. Because of increasing density of information and knowledge and the 'get-wise-easy' attitude of people, the 'digest' will become even more popular, but so will the specialist journal or magazine to meet the demand for expertise; one might predict that these specialist journals would go in and out of favour with unpredictable fashion.

Will there be a physically more active side to leisure in the home? The standard of living will continue to be excited up-wards by campaigns for greater productivity and full employ-ment with related waste-economy. Since salaries and wages will (as now) never quite equate with household material demands, the gap will be met by 'do it yourself' application as a leisure activity, *not* a domestic chore. Thus, handicrafts closely allied to home requirements – knitting and carpentry, for example – should become even more popular with the greater availability of home 'machine tools'. Machines will certainly be designed to make women less afraid of them and more skilled in their use.

Greater activity in model-making can be anticipated, and particularly of mobile models powered by small, powerful battery units. Although not directly related to adult leisure, the implications of the changes in children's toys in the past twenty years are significant; today's toys have reached considerable levels of technological skill and craftsmanship in, for example, the walking-talking doll, or modern railway sets. Succeeding toy fairs outdo each other in electronic and mechanical elaboration of products.

The influence of travel. Outside the home the car will provide a means for transporting people to leisure but motoring will not be considered a leisure pursuit in its own right. Travel to leisure will become more extensive, it will not be confined to the summer months, and it will take one farther and farther afield. The 'travel bug' could lead to design of equipment allowing transfer of the domestic scene from the rooted house to the mobile living space; for example, a shaped inflatable unit which packs into a car and is blown up by air-pump on site could constitute such a house. The desire of individuals to spend their week-end leisure away from home while still retaining the amenities of the home may presage a radical change in motor-car design besides giving impetus to development of the portable television and other normally 'fixed' leisure boxes.

Photography will become more of a family activity as a result of increasing travel. Cameras will be made 'fool-proof' and easy to manipulate in respect of range-finding and exposure, and instantaneous development of film without resort to the dark room or the professional photographer will make photography more attractive, particularly to women. The moving film will probably gain in popularity since it will be viewed as an addition to the television screen; movie cameras with associated sound recording will be popular.

Travel will have the important effect of 'internationalizing' leisure and particularly sport. Already international football, golf, and tennis are established, but such essentially national games as baseball (from the U.S.A.), judo (from Japan), or pelota (from Spain) may be taken up by countries where these games have not been generally practised or have been confined to the eccentric few. This feature may be accelerated by the shortening of communications through television or through political associations – in Britain the American N.A.T.O. bases have led to widening interest in basketball and baseball. The World Series (which is at present a U.S. monopoly) may more properly justify its name in 1984 through the competition of European communities and the Yankees or Dodgers.

Tools of the game. All games have their special tools. Because of increasing professionalism and the higher standards achieved by professionals through improved equipment and improved understanding of the techniques and skills of games, leisure amateurs will reach for higher standards by aping the professionals mainly through the medium of their equipment. In golf, we have had the steel shaft, scientifically redesigned heads of clubs, and changes in ball size, design, composition, and fabrication; in pole vaulting, the fibreglass pole; in tennis, new and still to be discovered synthetic fibres in a synthetic material frame will probably find application in tennis racquets and become much more effective weapons; for winter sports, skis will be improved in construction, surface treatment, and shape to facilitate movement and manoeuvrability; boats of revolutionary design (e.g. the home 'hovercraft') will favour fibreglass and new chemicals suited to moulding or forming, and sails will be of specially woven synthetic fibres.

Use of equipment of advanced design or materials will also obtain in such 'natural' activities as climbing and exploration under sea and under land (pot-holing) and will extend to specialized apparel. These items will be the subject of experiment and will derive much from advanced research into environmental medical studies. The knowledge which created the space suit may design the race suit.

Undoubtedly a new class of technologist will grow up who by scientific study will attempt to understand how records (and hence improved standards) can be achieved, so that by training to the tenets of newly acquired scientific knowledge of sport the professional and the amateur can improve their prowess. There have already been serious scientific studies of the drive in golf, the flight of the cricket ball, and the casting of flies. No sport will be sacred from scientific aids to improvement. Practice golf courses will operate with multi-view cameras taking records to show faults, and automatic cricket ball pitchers will bowl with variable speed, pitch, and spin.

There will be an increasing tendency to provide conditions for the practice of various sports and games throughout the whole year. An example is the honeycombed synthetic fibre as a permanent ski-slope independent of snowfalls. The alternative method of providing facilities independent of the climate is to enclose an area, and stadia showing considerable architectural and structural ingenuity will be built in great profusion. In part, this will derive from the existing '*in corpore sano*' features of education, so that its extension to adult leisure is not a very great step. One can expect a vast expansion in the numbers of swimming pools, tennis courts, dance halls, bowling alleys, and 'temples' for other activities demanding some physical output by the participant.

The recent popularity of the mechanized ten-pin bowling alley raises the question whether there will be a trend towards revival or modernization of ancient games. In this category would come archery, fencing, and wrestling. It may be significant that other classes of entertainment (dancing, singing, etc.) show a revival cycle of the order of twenty to thirty years.

Universal unthinking unction. But on the whole the next twenty years will see mainly a vast increase in unthinking, uncritical leisure based on activities which depend upon random chance and the satisfaction of mathematical probability, like bingo, roulette, and certain card games, and on forms of gambling sports – football pools, horse-racing, greyhound-racing. Since problems of chance are a respectable mathematical field of study, the universities of the Robbins era may well turn out mathematicians inventing games for gamblers.

I believe it is gambling which is likely to occupy the large mass of the population, cutting across all divisions of intellect, occupation, age, and sex.

There has been a general trend in this direction for many years now and there is nothing which suggests a reversal of this feature of social behaviour; in fact, in Britain, the Betting Act and custom have created conditions more likely to preserve this trend rather than militate against it. Many may prefer to see a more active or skilled or intellectual culture meet the leisure requirements of man in 1984, but the failure of the conventional cultural activities, music, theatre, art, etc., to exist in 1964 without subsidy does not afford hope for a different pattern in 1984.

A LABORATORY OF FUN

by Joan Littlewood

Politicians and educators, talking about increased leisure, mostly assume that people are so numb or servile that the hours in which they earn money need be made little more than hygienically bearable, while a new awareness is cultivated during the hours of leisure. This is to underestimate the future. Those who at present work in factories, mines, and offices will quite soon be able to live as only a few people now can: choosing their own congenial work, doing as much or as little of it as they like, and filling their leisure with whatever delights them. Those people who like fiddling with machinery and pressing buttons can service and press buttons in the robot-manned factories.

In London we are going to create a university of the streets – not a 'gracious' park but a foretaste of the pleasures of 1984. It will be a laboratory of pleasure, providing room for many kinds of action.

For example, the 'fun arcade' will be full of the games and tests that psychologists and electronics engineers now devise for the service of industry or war – now it will be piped through juke-boxes. In the music area we shall have, by day, instruments available, free instruction, recordings for anyone, classical, folk, jazz, and pop disc libraries; by night, jam sessions, jazz festivals, poetry and dance – every sort of popular dancing, formal or spontaneous.

There will be a 'science playground' where visitors can attend lecture-demonstrations supported by teaching films, closed-circuit television, and working models; by night, the area will become an *agora* or *kaffeeklatsch* where the Socrates, the Abelards, the Mermaid poets, the wandering scholars of the future, the mystics, the sceptics, and the sophists can dispute till dawn. An acting area will afford the therapy of theatre for everyone: men and women from factories, shops, and offices, bored with their daily routine, will be able to re-enact incidents from their own experience in burlesque and mime and gossip, so that they no longer accept passively whatever happens to them but wake to a critical awareness of reality, act out their subconscious fears and taboos, and perhaps are stimulated to social research.

A plastic area will be a place for uninhibited dabbling in wood, metal, paint, clay, stone, or textiles, for the rediscovery of the childhood experience of touching and handling, for constructing anything (useless or useful, to taste) from a giant crane to a bird-cage.

But the essence of the place will be its informality; nothing is obligatory, anything goes. There will be no permanent structures. Nothing is to last for more than ten years, some things not even ten days: no concrete stadia, stained and cracking; no legacy of noble contemporary architecture, quickly dating; no municipal geranium-beds or fixed teak benches.

With informality goes flexibility. The 'areas' that have been listed are not segregated enclosures. The whole plan is open, but on many levels. So the greatest pleasure of traditional parks is preserved – the pleasure of strolling casually, looking in at one or other of these areas or (if this is preferred) settling down for several hours of work-play.

Besides the activities already briefly outlined, there will be plenty to engage imagination and enlarge experience. At various points, sheltered or open, there will be screens on which closed-circuit television will show, without editing or art, whatever is going on at a number of places in and out of London, and in the complex itself: it will be possible to see coal-mines, woodmen, and dockers actually at work; Monkey Hill, the aquarium, or the insect house at the Zoo; the comings and goings outside a local authority rest-centre, a Salvation Army hostel, the casualty ward of a hospital, or a West End club; newspanels will bring world and local news.

The curiosity that many people feel about their neighbours' lives can be satisfied instructively and with greater immediacy than in any documentary film ... and an occasion of major popular interest – a Cup Final, happenings of international interest, or a royal funeral – would be presented on screens of maximum size. The visitor can enjoy a sense of identity with the world about him.

Many who start by wandering half-attentively, or even sceptically, through the complex will be drawn into these and other elementary exercises in social observation. In what has been called the acting area, for instance, there will be no rigid division between performers and audience – a generalization of the technique used in Theatre Workshop for many years.

As I have described it, it may seem very busy, yet the general atmosphere will be one of relaxation and – equally important and now technically possible – there will be zones of quiet for those who don't feel like listening to music or taking part actively in all that is going on. Here they can watch, lounge about and find enjoyment in wasting time.

ARCHITECT'S NOTE

by Cedric Price

An architect elaborates on the design of the 'Fun-Palace' envisaged by Joan Littlewood

This complex, which enables self-participatory education and entertainment can only work – and then only for a finite time – if it is not only accessible to those living and working in the immediate neighbourhood but also, through its varied communication links, accessible as a regional and national amenity.

The siting exploits existing communication networks and gives a clue to the potential enrichment of life through increasing mobility at present unrealized in large urban communities. The

sense of confinement on the site is reduced by the deliberate extension of the visible limits.

The activities designed for the site should be experimental,
the place itself expendable and changeable. The organization
of space and the objects occupying it should, on the one hand,
challenge the participants' mental and physical dexterity and,
on the other, allow for a flow of space and time, in which passive
and active pleasure is provoked.

The ephemeral nature of the architecture is a major element

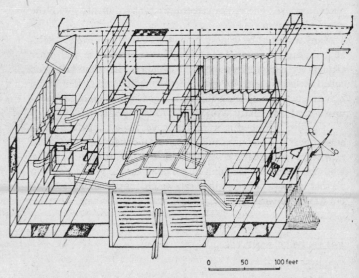

0   50   100 feet

FIG. 1 Isometric diagram showing full width and two out of the fourteen
bays in the length of the complex.

in the design, making possible the use of materials and techniques
normally excluded from the building industry. Charged static-
vapour zones, optical barriers, warm-air curtains, and fog-
dispersal plant are some of the methods employed, together with
vertical and horizontal lightweight blinds.

Within the complex, the public moves about, above the largely
unobstructed ground-level deck, on ramps, moving walkways,
catwalks, and radial escalators. All such equipment is capable of

rearrangement – allowing multidirectional movement and random
pedestrian grouping, yet capable of programming. The complex
itself, having no doorways, enables one to choose one's own
route and degree of involvement with the activities. Although
the framework will remain a constant size, the total volume in
use may vary, thus presenting a changing scene even to the
frequent user. While individual enclosures such as theatre areas,
workshops, or restaurants have their own particular controlled
environment, the total volume is capable of resisting or modifying
adverse climatic conditions.

The nature of the enclosures and the degree of control required for these activities are so varied – including as they do
large-volume activities such as rallies, concerts, conferences,
theatre, and screenings – that each is built up of separate units
('walls', 'floors', 'ceilings') as required. Inflatable enclosures are
also used. The smaller enclosures are more likely to be self-
contained: these are built-up standard-unit 'boxes' of reinforced
plastic and aluminium, set on and serviced from open 'decks'.
The construction and arrangement of such enclosures, together
with the movement and positioning of fittings and equipment,
are achieved by a permanent travelling gantry crane spanning
the whole structure.

The movement of staff, piped services, and escape routes are
provided for within the open-frame, protected steel stanchions
of the superstructure and cross-connected at service basement
level, where service access and parking are located, together with
the necessary plant.

The whole complex provides valuable site-testing conditions
for a wide range of materials, equipment, and constructional
techniques.

Trade

FOOTLOOSE INDUSTRIES AND THE LURE OF THE SUN

by Professor L. Dudley Stamp

There are diverse forces at work which promise to effect some major changes in the world distribution of industry before 1984. Some of those forces are economic, but by no means all, and not all pull in the same direction.

A high place must be given to national pride and prestige. The emergent nations, noticing that the great powers are in the main industrial nations, are apt to equate national prestige with industrialization. They believe that to remain a primary producer, especially in agriculture, is to lag behind in the race despite the fact that the most pressing need of all – as, for example, in India – is increased efficiency in farming and food production, without which an ill-fed people cannot hope to progress in other directions. But a factory in the town has become as much a status-symbol as television in the home. Inevitably 1984 will witness the wider spread of piecemeal industrialization of this sort, with the unhappy accompaniment of ill-spent subsidies to maintain small units and high tariff barriers to keep out the rival products.

It seems almost hopeless to visualize a common-sense world, where a world government would secure for all a rising standard of living by concentrating primary and secondary production in those parts where natural geographic and economic conditions are the most favourable. Contrary to the widely held belief, natural factors are more, not less, important today than in the past. We live in a world of cut-throat competition. With instantaneous communication by radio, happenings in most distant regions are known within minutes the world over. No place on Earth is beyond reach of modern high-speed means of transport and, provided a local product has sufficient intrinsic value, it is no longer denied access to the world's markets. In medieval England, if a village wanted to eat wheaten bread, the villagers had to grow the wheat themselves, even though adverse soil and climate resulted in low yields. As transport and communications improved, reliance was placed on the cheaper, more efficient production in those parts of the country, or even abroad, where natural physical conditions were more suitable.

In varying degree it is the same for all production, primary and secondary. Except for artificial man-made barriers, production would be concentrated where the natural geographical environment is most propitious. While it is self-evident that wheat is best produced where soil, climate, and terrain most favour high yields and top qualities, the natural factors governing rational industrial location may not be so obvious.

A first need is energy. So long as a fall of water provided motive power for water mills, falls on any major river – but especially when a navigable waterway stretched downstream – encouraged the siting of a mill-town. Herein we see the origin of Sheffield or Sioux Falls, the Fall line towns of America's eastern seaboard, or Ottawa, or Switzerland's Schaffhausen. At the time when wood and charcoal were major sources of energy, accessible forests were a locational factor as in the old Wealden iron industry. With the swing to coal as a major fuel associated with the Industrial Revolution, there was the migration of industry to the coalfields and the rise of their factory towns.

We live now in an age when continued discoveries of vast resources of natural oil and gas have eclipsed the lead of coal. Both oil and gas can be transported great distances by pipeline; pipeline owners can and do act as common carriers. Crude oil is more easily handled than the refined products (e.g. petrol) so that the general tendency is to refine in the importing country. The main point, however, is that the oilfields themselves rarely give rise to industrial areas; the more oil is used, the greater is the mobility of industries using oil as a fuel.

Water power is now normally converted to electricity which must be generated on the spot and which is expensive to transport. For the most part industry is brought to the source of power or to some geographically convenient locality – such as a deepwater sheltered anchorage to receive heavy raw material –

not more than 200 or 300 miles at the most from the source of power. Systems of distribution by high voltage lines improve, but the cost of installation is high. The example afforded by Kitimat on Canada's far western seaboard, smelting imported bauxite into aluminium, will be multiplied. Inevitably, Jinja in Uganda, the Damodar Valley in India, the Katanga, and the attraction of the Kariba will be matched in many of the present underdeveloped countries. In the long run they may be the fortunate ones; coal and oil are exhaustible, water power is being constantly renewed.

In so far as local mineral resources influence the siting of industries, we can expect the existing major centres to hold their own, being joined by other regions at present underdeveloped – like the Damodar valley and Katanga, which I have mentioned. However, both modern transport and the trend to sophisticated industries (electronics, drugs, aircraft manufacture, etc.), where materials are used in very small quantities, mean that many factories can be sited almost anywhere (the factory estate at Shannon airport is one of many demonstrations of this new freedom). Other factors will have as much influence as mineral resources.

At the present time we are only just beginning to appreciate the importance of a very old yet very new factor – climate. Many contend that man is, by nature, a tropical animal. He has almost no protective covering of fur; the great civilizations of early days, such as Harrappa, Babylon, Nineveh, and Egypt, were all in the tropics or tropical margins. As man learnt to heat his home, centres of civilization shifted to Greece and Rome, but we should remind ourselves that the Romans did not consider Britain a fit country in which to live without central heating. Adequate home heating alone makes possible life in the winter of North America or Russia. The new weapon is air-conditioning. It is more than just the creation of an artificial climate in which it is pleasant to live; we can make the climate in which the human body and brain function most effectively; we can make the climate, with control of humidity and temperature, in which the most delicate manufacturing operations can be properly performed.

We think in terms of irrigating the arid lands; bringing water that the farmers may be assured of a harvest and freedom from hunger. But only a fraction of that amount of water would be needed to support an urban civilization in the desert. Already there is a shift of industry to new towns in sunny dry lands – air-conditioned homes, offices, and factories, glorious sunshine, lovely watered gardens. The cities in the arid south-western States of the U.S.A. are growing three times as rapidly as those in other parts of the country.

A fifth of the Earth's surface is too hot and arid for cultivation; here is plenty of room for industrial towns. We need much new thinking on use of water resources. It is scarcely too much to suggest that the Aswan High Dam is a tragedy, not because of the monuments of the past doomed to be covered by the waters, but because it is out of date before it is begun. Much of the water brought by the Nile is already lost by evaporation, more will be lost from the huge reservoir, perhaps 50 or 60 per cent. It should have been brought by pipeline from the source mountains – no loss by evaporation, perfect control.

Water does not, then, produce a major obstacle to the development of industrial towns, but a seaside location is favoured by need of abundant industrial water, as for cooling, disposal of effluent, and for ready import of raw materials and export of finished products. The cheap production of fresh water from salt water is surely around the corner.

Summarizing: by 1984 we may expect a continued swing away from coal, perhaps already away from oil, to hydro-electricity (not forgetting tidal power) and possibly solar energy. We may expect a gathering movement of industrial towns to the sun, especially to coastal situations in the arid lands.

CONCEIVABLE PATTERNS OF TRADE

by Professor Thorkil Kristensen

Secretary-General of the Organisation for Economic Cooperation and Development, Paris

Does it make sense at all in early 1964 to discuss what trade might be in the world of 1984? Is not the amount of uncertainty such as to make it a very risky undertaking? It obviously is very risky, if only because trade will depend to a large extent on the policies pursued by governments over the next twenty years, and while one can ascertain more or less clear trends in technical development or population growth, it is hardly meaningful to talk about trends in policies. However, I have accepted to write this article because I think that it does make sense to try. Human action is based, more than we perhaps know, on our ideas about the future, and these ideas in their turn are based on past experience. This will also be true of future action in the field of policy making. Therefore, though it is probably a rather hopeless task to predict future *party policies*, it may not be quite so meaningless to make guesses about future *trade policy*, which will at least to some extent be guided by facts that are partly predictable, because they are partly beyond the field of influence of political vicissitudes.

The following considerations are based on the assumption that there will be no third World War (using nuclear weapons) before 1984. Only on this assumption does it make sense to undertake guesswork or projections. Now, if peaceful co-existence is to continue for another twenty years, it seems on the whole likely that it will become rather more than less peaceful, compared with what it is today. This again means that the political obstacles to trade between the East and the West should rather become weaker than stronger over the next twenty years.

Another assumption will be that the differences between the existing politico-economical structures of the various countries will on the whole become less pronounced than they are today. Roughly speaking there are three groups of countries in the present world. These are:

(1) *the industrial market economies*, mainly in Western Europe, North America, and Oceania, plus Japan;

(2) *the centralized economies*, i.e. the Socialist countries; and finally

(3) *the less-developed countries*.

We know that the last will on the whole become more industrialized, which means that their systems will become more similar to those of group (1) or, in some cases maybe, to those of group (2). Now, it seems likely that state intervention will continue to increase in group (1) in the foreseeable future while, at the same time, the countries in group (2) will be giving somewhat more freedom to individual enterprises and also will partly introduce trade and payments systems more similar to the Western pattern than before. It is, therefore, assumed that in their structure and their politico-economical systems the three groups of countries will in 1984 be less different from one another than in 1964.

We should now look at two basic facts from which we can not only ascertain the present position but also have some reasonably well-founded ideas about the trends that are likely to prevail over the next twenty years.

There is, first, *world population*. According to existing estimates, it can be assumed to change between 1964 and 1984 very roughly as follows:

	Populations in billions	
	1964	1984
Developed countries (30 per cent increase)	1·0	1·3
Less-developed countries (60 per cent increase)	2·2	3·5
World (50 per cent increase)	3·2	4·8

The developed countries are the countries of Europe, North America, and Oceania, plus Japan and the U.S.S.R. The contrast between their relatively slow population growth and the explosive growth in the poor countries will be one of the most striking and decisive facts of the next twenty years.

The other basic fact is the existence of *the two gaps*. The level of incomes is higher in the industrial market economies than in the centralized economies, but this gap is likely to narrow to some extent because the Soviet economy, though growing somewhat slower than in earlier years, is still growing faster than the economies of Western countries in general.

Much more important, however, is the income gap between the industrial or developed countries and the less-developed nations. Here, the gap is enormous and it has been widening in recent years. The widening may go on for some years to come – though one would hope for not too many years. By 1984 the income gap between the rich and the poor countries will probably be wider than now in absolute terms. In relative terms it may not be radically different from what it is today.

On the basis of the facts and assumptions outlined above, can we draw any conclusions, however tentative, about the conceivable trade patterns of 1984? Let us try.

(1) There will be more trade than now, certainly in absolute terms, but probably also as compared with total production, because countries will become more industrialized and experience shows that, the more countries industrialize, the more they trade with one another. Two raw material producers do not have much to sell to each other. As the politico-economic structures of the three groups of countries are likely to be less different than today, that too should facilitate trade between them; in turn, increased trade will contribute to a further reduction of remaining differences. With exports of goods will go exports of techniques, of ideas, and of ways of life.

(2) There will probably be more East–West trade, in relative as well as in absolute terms. If it is true that the political obstacles to this kind of trade will on the whole be weakened and the two systems become somewhat more like one another, trade is likely to grow. The Socialist economies will probably find it in their interest to share the benefits of trade with other countries more than they do today and, if the gap between them and the Western nations becomes narrower, they may become more courageous in reducing their restrictions.

(3) The present less-developed countries will probably trade more with one another than they do today, partly because they will become less closely tied to the old metropolitan countries and partly because they will become more industrialized. This development may be further enhanced by the establishment of trading groups among these countries, like the Latin American Free Trade Area, and the Central American Common Market.

(4) What will trade between the industrial and the less-developed countries be? Certainly larger than today, and it will consist more of industrial goods, since raw materials represent a decreasing element in total production as all products become more and more highly manufactured. The less-developed countries will have to develop their industries by means of their

enormous – and cheap – labour force because the revenue from their raw material exports will be insufficient.

Paradoxically enough, the industrial countries, while buying more industrial goods from the poor countries, may be selling more *food* to them, especially to the densely populated Asian countries. This is already beginning, and the population explosion mentioned above makes it likely that it will continue. It is not inconceivable that the movement of great quantities of food from the rich countries to the poor will be one of the fundamental features of the trade pattern of 1984. But the poor nations will need more aid and private capital imports from the industrial countries in order to be able to buy the food and the investment goods they need. Aid, in preventing the income gap from becoming too wide, may then further trade.

SELF-SUFFICIENCY OR INTERDEPENDENCE?

by Eric Wyndham White

Executive Secretary of the General Agreement on Tariffs and Trade, Geneva

There are some underlying elements and characteristics of international trade that allow predictions to be put forward on a reasonable and defensible basis. A notable post-war economic phenomenon has been the trend towards regionalism. This has been reflected in such regional groups as the European Economic Community and the European Free Trade Association in Western Europe, COMECON in Eastern Europe, the Latin American Free Trade Area, the Equatorial Customs Union, and other forms of economic association in Africa, and in the consideration being given to closer economic cooperation in Asia. Political, economic, and technological factors have gone hand in hand to bring about this development.

A feature of these groups is that none of them is near to self-sufficiency. On the contrary, most of them depend heavily on trade with 'third countries'; for example, no less than sixty per cent of total trade in the case of the E.E.C., and eighty per cent in the case of E.F.T.A., is represented by trade with third countries. In this connexion it is worth while remarking that two of the biggest economic entities in the world, namely the United States and the U.S.S.R., are becoming more, rather than less, dependent on an increasing participation in international trade.

By 1984, the pattern of production, marketing, trade, and so on in regional groups will be such that there will be a high degree of interdependence between the constituent countries of each group. The important question, for world trade generally, is whether intra-regional interdependence will be translated into increasing interdependence on a world plane or whether, with the possibility of more and more national economies being absorbed into such groupings, the result will be a few very big, largely self-sufficient, economic units, with only minimal trade between them.

It is reasonable to assume that, as at present, these big economic units will be far from a situation of self-sufficiency and that the trend will be towards growing interdependence. In fact, the indications are that technological developments, not to mention possible political considerations, will result in a situation which will make the present system and structure of groupings too narrow. In the sense purely of economic and trade policy, the need for tariff and other protective measures will increasingly be seen to be illogical; in this connexion, one might quote the example, on the country level, of France and Germany, two highly industrialized and competitive countries which have found it possible, through their membership of the E.E.C., progressively to eliminate barriers on the trade between them. Moreover, as a result of the wide dissemination of technical know-how and the intense research which is being undertaken in all major industrialized countries, any disequilibrium between these countries as regards technical skills and competitive ability is likely to disappear.

If this prognosis is a reasonable one, it would therefore seem to me that, by 1984, there will be large economic units or groups which will already have developed a considerable measure of division of labour and increased trade between them. While there will undoubtedly remain basic political differences, the influence of such factors as modern conditions of production and marketing are likely to bring about a narrowing of differences of approach and philosophy, at least in the economic sector.

Governmental policy decisions and direction in the broadest sense will be necessary to guide economic units of this size, and there will also need to be increased cooperation in the international field in trade, financial, and technical matters. Nevertheless, within these broad governmental policies, the free play of economic forces and the cost and price mechanisms are likely to operate more widely and will be a further factor contributing to more extensive trading relations.

Undoubtedly there will be difficulties of adaptation in certain sectors of industry in the developed countries but, despite the often politically sensitive character of these difficulties, such adjustments are an inevitable corollary to economic development. It might be relevant to point out that, should additional adjustments be required in the industrialized countries to permit a liberal policy towards imports of manufactures from the less-developed countries, such adjustments would be of a minor character when compared with the overall pattern of adjustments required for economic growth.

As regards the agricultural sector, trade in agricultural products may well, by 1984, move into a position very different from that of today. The projected growth in populations and the expected substantial increases in standards of living, particularly in the less-developed countries, are likely to create greatly increased demand for foodstuffs.

By 1984 there will still be a gap between the income and standards of living of some parts of the world as compared with others. The important question is: will this gap be narrowed? At the present time there is a tendency for it to get bigger, but the freer exchange of goods and resources which should result from the developments I have already outlined can be expected to have brought about, by 1984, a situation which will facilitate a greater transfer of resources from the richer to the poorer areas of the world and which will accelerate the diversification of these poorer economies. As a result, while the gap will continue to exist, it should be considerably reduced by 1984.

An essential element in this situation will be the availability of markets for the products resulting from industrialization and diversification of production in the less-developed countries, so as to permit these countries substantially to increase their earnings of foreign exchange to finance their imports of capital goods. Already there is the tendency for the industrialized countries to concentrate on capital-intensive rather than labour-intensive production and, as the move by these countries into the production of more sophisticated goods gathers momentum, this should make room in their markets for increasing quantities of such products as light engineering and consumer goods from the less-developed countries.

International Relations

UNIVERSAL NON-ALIGNMENT AND METHODICAL DECISION-MAKING

by Dr J. W. Burton

Faculty of Laws, University College, London

What will be the features of world society in 1984? One assumption must be made for our present purposes; there will meanwhile be no all-out thermonuclear war.

Speculation about development in the next twenty years could be on the basis of a guessing game in which one made guesses about the relative power positions, the nature of alliances, whether China and India might be in conflict, whether unification of Germany will take place and lead to an altered power situation, and so on. What is quite certain is that even if in this game-playing we cover a very large number of possible situations, we will not think to play the $n + 1$ game – the situation which will actually occur. All the earnest game-playing that went on in the United States in academic and military circles in the late 1950s did not include the game in which Castro would successfully invite the assistance of the Soviet Union, and the placement of rockets in Cuba.

It is perhaps less fun, but more useful, to speculate on the basis only of long-term trends which seem to have some persistence and continuity, and which are, in a sense, measurable. For example, we are capable of saying something specific about population growth and the exploitation of resources, both of which have political implications. We are able to say something fairly reliable about scientific developments, and particularly developments in communications of all kinds, and those, too, alter relations between States. Of more concern in predicting what world society might look like in 1984 are other trends, the continuing existence of which is in very little doubt, but which may not be as subject to numerical treatment.

For example, the modern state has been developing over a period of hundreds of years, and there have been many continuous features including the growth of what is termed 'nationalism'. We understand generally what we mean by this term; we know, to take one instance, that nationalism includes a desire to be independent. The existence of national defences, the desire for independent deterrents, the reluctance to accept outside control by another nation or a group of nations, all have roots in this sentiment we call nationalism in the modern State. The desire of sovereign States, large or small, to pursue their own independent policies is an important factor in the modern world, and there is no reason to believe it will not continue to be so.

A second and related long-term trend is the tendency for international organizations to be based more on principles of consent, and less on a so-called collective security that implies some capability of enforcement upon member States by a universal organization. When the League of Nations Covenant was drafted, and at San Francisco when the United Nations Charter was drafted, there was still the lingering hope that there could be a universal collective security, and a hope that this could be one step toward an ideal of world government on the model of a municipal society. The long-term trend, however, is in the direction of a type of international organization based on consent and with no powers other than recommendation, and which does little more than enable the relatively inefficient bilateral relationship of States to be organized on a multilateral basis. It includes centralized administration, and an increasing number of both regional and functional institutions.

One would anticipate, therefore, that by 1984 there will be a growth of independent deterrents, nuclear and non-nuclear, in those countries which have the industrial capability. Within the framework of H-bomb deterrence, there will be a second system of A-bomb deterrence. There will be the further development of independent policies, and even, perhaps, a new form of isolationism in which States endeavour to pursue their interests independently, without being involved in the conflicts of other States. Certainly the thermonuclear powers can no longer afford the luxury of alliances which draw them into conflict over matters not vital to them, and technically they no longer require them. By 1984, the smaller nuclear powers also will be far more interested in pursuing their interests by means which do not involve them in alliances and in power balances, and this means, of course, that they will be paying far greater attention to the complicated processes of decision-making and to the responses of other countries to their national policies, and will be conducting far more intensive negotiation and communication with each other. This relationship of major powers will be held stable, firstly by nuclear deterrents, and secondly by the decision-making processes which nuclear deterrents have forced on all countries. As a consequence of these processes, change by peaceful means will take place, for example revision of terms of trade between States or social change within States which might otherwise have been prevented by foreign intervention.

Within this stability, there are likely to be numerous small conflicts. During this next twenty years tremendous adjustments will be required in relationships between smaller States consequent upon the creation of independent States in place of former colonial empires. Boundary adjustments will cause many conflicts, and there will be attempts to create federations perhaps by negotiation, perhaps by conquest, and perhaps by combinations of the two. There will be racial conflict; South Africa may be one centre, and perhaps the United States another, and racial conflicts will not be confined to races of different colour. Prompted by these conflict-situations there will be further development of regional arrangements outside the United Nations which will take an active part in the resolution of conflict.

Conflict in Africa, Asia, and the Middle East will be aggravated by a growing awareness of the inequality of incomes and opportunities that exist throughout the world. Despite aid, and changes in terms of trade, the affluent States will be becoming more affluent, and the underdeveloped States will be hardpressed even to maintain existing living standards as their populations increase. Population control will not be effective within this twenty-year period. One could reasonably predict the emergence by 1984 of the classical 'have' and 'have-not' conflict, with the Western countries acting in defence of their interests against the pressures of Asia, Africa, and Latin America. Yet perhaps 1984 will be too soon for an organized confrontation of this order; there must first be a great deal of industrial development in the dissatisfied nations, including China, before this can occur.

1984, therefore, is likely to be a world society in which independent sovereign States are each pursuing their own independent policies, a situation in which all States are 'non-aligned', not only in respect of the conflict between the thermonuclear powers, but in respect of each other. The controls on these independent foreign policies of major States will be the two important factors of credibility and consensus. No threat, no policy can achieve its purpose unless it is credible, and by 1984 policy will achieve its purpose only if it relates to a world consensus. The assumption was made above that there would be no all-out thermonuclear war. If there is no such war during this twenty-year period, by 1984 we will know far more about the nature both of credibility and of this consensus, and therefore about the conduct of foreign policy.

SCIENTISTS AS PEACEMAKERS

by Professor Joseph Rotblat
Secretary-General, Pugwash Continuing Committee

The development of nuclear weapons and of rapid means of their delivery has completely altered the factors governing international relations. For the first time in history it has become possible for mankind to be destroyed as a result of an international conflict. It is quite likely that, with the further progress of science and technology during the next twenty years, the means of wholesale destruction will become much more simplified and accessible even to small and less-developed nations.

Under these conditions, the only chance for mankind to survive is to abolish altogether the present division into a large number of sovereign states and to replace it by a federation of all nations under one world authority, suitably organized to prevent any of its members acquiring hegemony, whilst at the same time leaving them freedom to pursue their own way of life.

This ideal state of affairs will not be reached by 1984, if indeed we manage to avoid a nuclear holocaust. We shall probably have several narrow escapes from Cuban-like brinkmanships, and although these will intensify the realization of the need for a united world system, the inherent distrust and suspicion with which the present generation has been brought up, coupled with the too slow adaptation of politicians to new situations, will prove too great a hindrance. However, a number of important steps, which will greatly improve international relations, will have been taken, mainly on the initiative and efforts of scientists.

The cosmopolitan nature of science, the universality of its methods and its ethics, and the consequent close and friendly relations which have always existed amongst scientists of different nations, make science the natural and best medium for international understanding. This role of science has acquired much more cogency in recent years for two reasons: first, because science has been acknowledged the most important force in the development of the human community, and secondly, because the trend of scientific growth is such as to make international collaboration essential. By 1984 there will be in existence a number of truly international scientific projects, including a multi-billion volt particle accelerator, an institute for fundamental biology which by that time will also use huge machines, and a world health research centre. These projects will involve not only a vast expenditure – which, following the initiative of President de Gaulle, will be provided from the moneys saved on defence, as disarmament gradually progresses – but also a large number of scientists, technicians, and administrative staff, drawn from all nations of the world, thus creating excellent opportunities for international collaboration.

Moreover, the agreement, which will be reached long before then, that scientists from the advanced countries should as a rule spend a year in the underdeveloped countries, before settling down to an academic career – with a reciprocal arrangement for scientists from the poor countries – will further strengthen international collaboration, apart from being of direct benefit to world development.

However, the contribution of scientists towards improving

international relations will go well beyond these scientific
projects.

International conferences of scientists, to discuss problems of
world security and the application of the scientific approach to
the solution of political issues, will play a role of increasing
importance in world affairs, following the success of the Pugwash
Conferences. A direct contribution to the lessening of tension in
areas of chronic conflict will be made at these conferences by the
initiation of scientific collaboration between the countries concerned, for example between India and Pakistan, and between
the Arab countries and Israel. The joining of China in the disarmament negotiations of the United Nations will be a consequence of the understanding on these matters first reached by
scientists at the international conferences. Berlin will cease to be
the main obstacle to a settlement in Europe, by implementing
the plan put forward some years ago to set up there an International Science Centre, followed by the transfer to Berlin of
the headquarters of the United Nations.

As the number of scientists participating in such international
discussions, or in study groups in their own countries, will increase there will emerge numerous new and original ideas for the
establishment of a secure world system. Statesmen and politicians
will gradually become more aware of the importance of the
scientific attitude in solving international problems. Scientists
will be called upon increasingly to advise governments and to
accept official or semi-official posts. These advisers will attend
the international conferences as observers, but the bulk of
scientists participating in them will consist of uncommitted
individuals, still active in research work in their own subjects.

The main preoccupation of these conferences and study
groups will be research into the problems of peace: how to
maintain order in a world in which stockpiles of weapons held
by individual nations will be eliminated but the potential to
re-build them in a short time greatly increased; how to avoid
conflict in the face of still existing – although diminishing –
economic and ideological differences; how to establish an attitude
of mind that war is not a necessary component of civilization. To
prove that such research is not merely academic, the scientists
will have to apply their general conclusions to specific cases as

they may occur in life. Eventually, a standing Committee, or Council, with a frequently renewed membership but always consisting of experienced and independent scientists (any official appointment will mean automatic disqualification from the Council), will be set up to keep the political situation continually under review. This will be based on a rational assessment of material provided by computers located all over the world in order to sample trends and attitudes of populations. A conflict arising in any part of the world will be immediately investigated and a solution, founded entirely on an objective analysis, will be worked out and published. These pronouncements will be unofficial and carry no executive power, but the pressure of public opinion, trustful in the integrity of scientists, will compel even reluctant governments to pay attention to them and use their findings as a basis for the solution of the conflict.

As a result of these efforts, the distrust and fears among nations will be drastically reduced, and by 1984 the scientists will have achieved their major goal, the drafting and general acceptance of a new system of education, based on the ideals of fundamental common interests of the human species, and on the development of a sense of belonging to mankind as a whole Thus, by the end of this century, when the generation brought up in this new spirit will take over, the establishment of a World Authority, and a system of sufficient stability to cope with the problems created by the further progress of science will follow as a matter of course.

WORLD DEVELOPMENT: THE CRUCIAL CHOICE

by Professor M. S. Thacker

Planning Commission, Government of India

One does not have to be an optimist to forecast progressive improvement in international collaboration in science and technology by 1984. But will such improvement be accompanied by determined action to raise the living conditions of the people in the developing areas of the world? That is a crucial question; for if it does not happen – and it has to start happening now to ensure minimum standards of living for people in emerging countries – one may well wonder what hope there is for peace and continued civilized existence.

The United Nations conference at Geneva in 1963 on the application of science and technology for the benefit of less-developed areas showed how applied science could be the most powerful force in the world for raising standards of living. The conclusion may not have been new; but on that occasion spokesmen of ninety-six developed and developing nations expressed with unanimity the view that the rising tide of expectation of the people over vast areas of the world must be satisfied, and science and technology must be put to work for their benefit.

The accent must be on action. Meetings and discussions we have had before. The 1963 Conference was preceded by others with specific objectives; peaceful uses of atomic energy; new sources of energy; conservation of natural resources; and so on. All of them have emphasized the need for collaboration to achieve definite ends. The several international agencies of the United Nations are also in some measure tackling problems in their respective areas of operation – education, science, health, agriculture, labour, etc. International scientific councils and unions are also helping. Relations between scientists of different nationalities are becoming more and more intimate. Scientists from many different countries take part in projects like the International Years of the Quiet Sun and the Indian Ocean Expedition. International agreements govern space exploration and polar expeditions, and in all fields of science there is evidence of ever-closer collaboration among nations. These are not just 'straws in the wind'. I see them as the milestones of advance on the road of international development.

The projects which are currently receiving collective attention are important. Moreover, they are in the true tradition of science, for the Book of Science contains names from all the main regions of the world. Not so, unhappily, the Book of Technology!

The nations which have achieved prosperity have done so by putting knowledge into action, developing technologies directed to the efficient utilization of natural resources. The technologies, affording the know-how for productive endeavour, have established thriving industries. And now they must be introduced into the vast developing regions of the world. The conditions must be created in those regions so that not only can imported technologies take root, but new technologies can be generated to meet local situations. It is a challenging task. International action is required; equally, it is the obligation of individual developing countries to bring about necessary basic social changes.

There are several technical problems of global significance awaiting solution: nuclear fusion technology is one example, sea-bottom mining for mineral resources is another. But the biggest among them, into which all these merge and which dwarfs everything else in comparison – whether we consider human values, political implications, or the intellectual challenge – is the need rapidly to improve conditions in the poorer half of the world. The rate at which populations are expanding is a measure of what we must do just to prevent things growing worse and makes one apprehensive that the growth in numbers will far outpace economic development. Even the provision of essential requirements, like food, clothing, and shelter, may remain a distant dream in 1984.

Can one say that the problems posed by the developing areas are only their own concern? Oases of prosperity cannot exist amidst vast areas of hunger, poverty, and disease without dire consequences for all.

Today we do not need to be convinced that science and technology can bring prosperity. Advanced countries provide an object lesson. Not only that; the awareness of the possibilities which science and technology hold for promoting human welfare is widespread and, in the emerging countries, not only do expectations run high but people become restive.

I see the next twenty years being devoted to planned action to use the benefits of science and technology to abolish scarcities wherever they exist, with all nations joining forces to solve the problems. The alternative is unthinkable, but that by itself will not prevent it. Some of the features of the world of 1984 are predictable from present technological trends; others will depend on scientific leaps about which we can only guess. But the most important aspect of all – whether or not the people of the world are to be well-fed, healthy, and able to enjoy life – depends entirely on the choices made now by those men in all countries who are in a position to act if they want to do so.

International action alone can produce results; good international relations are not enough. And action will not only demand a sense of urgency but will require resources and men. Today the climate for collective international action is more propitious than ever before. One can but hope that all men of wisdom, goodwill, and capacity for action, in all walks of life, will unite with this simple purpose; to raise, in the next twenty years, more than two thirds of the world's population to a condition compatible with human dignity.

Britain

COPING WITH 'PROGRESS'

by Sir George Thomson, F.R.S.

There are some obvious challenges which Britain has to face in the next twenty years, and also certain new possibilities which one can see coming along from recent scientific developments. The possibilities do not precisely match the challenges – it would be amazingly good luck if they did – but where they do it is reasonable to suppose they will be applied.

The outstanding challenges arise from the need to cope with very complex and rapidly changing situations caused by the application of science. Such are automation with its social implications, the congestion of our cities accompanied by the destruction of the countryside, and the problem of education for a new world.

The first, automation, is the direct consequence of advances in 'intelligent' control systems which, expressed in various forms, are also the greatest of the new possibilities. Automation is, of course, far more than an improvement in machine tools to make them work with fewer people. It implies the control of complicated interlocking processes, typified by what has to be done in an oil refinery producing a variety of products for which there may be a variable demand. Ability to do this kind of thing depends on advances in what one may call the 'technique of thought' which are capable of much greater extension; to management in general, to planning, and even to politics.

Like many innovations, this one started under the pressure of fear of war, in the invention of operational research in Britain twenty-five years ago, and in the recent use of the 'theory of games' in the Pentagon. The electronic computer is the ideal instrument for the purpose because it can deal with complexity (situations in real life are almost always complex), but it is only the instrument; the ideas are deeper. They require the development of means of analysing complex situations so that the most likely to succeed of many conceivable courses of action can be found. I believe the next twenty years will see both a great improvement in these methods and a great increase in the extent to which they are used in ordinary business and even in politics.

Management is going to be intensely interesting. It will require a larger and larger proportion of the working force – a kind of Parkinson's law, if you like, but one without some of the more unpleasant implications of that great generalization. In a world in which it will be increasingly difficult to find work for the not-so-bright, managers and those engaged in research and development will share with artists and the mothers of children under nine the privilege of working more than the short standard hours, and will enjoy it.

I am inclined to trust this new trend of thought to get us out of the socially more unpleasant consequences of automation. Perhaps leisure will not turn out so terrible as it now appears. To the Greeks and to the author of *Genesis* it was work, not leisure, that was the curse.

Everyone agrees our towns are a mess and probably getting worse. This is not wholly due to the motor-car, though a good deal of it is. Modern buildings, especially large ones, in Britain seem unable to incorporate new materials to the best aesthetic advantage. This is not so everywhere. For example, the new Dulles Airport for Washington is only one of several outstandingly beautiful new buildings in the U.S.A. There are likely to be startling new materials before 1984, since the possibilities of really strong solids are now well realized. These will be perhaps ten times as strong in tension as any present-day engineering materials, though not in compression, which is mostly a matter of stiffness, not ultimate strength. They should lead to lighter and more graceful structures. If ropes and fabrics are very strong and struts only as at present, the problems of building will become more like those of rigging a sailing ship.

The motor-car menace is really a matter for economists and sociologists rather than for scientists. I can only record my hope – far from a firm belief – that it will not take us twenty years longer to discover that it is a mistake to use roads to provide parking space for commuters.

I fear the countryside has 'had it'. Every improvement in transport makes it possible for people to live farther from their work, and many like to do so. A rising standard of living, which one may reasonably assume, will make matters worse. England isn't big enough for 50 million country-lovers. Nothing but a drastic reduction in birth rate coupled with a prolonged depression could save it, and such a cure is surely worse than the disease. One crumb of comfort: if, as seems fairly likely, superconductors can be used in heavy engineering, high-tension cables will go underground and pylons may disappear.

Having worked all my life in universities, I cannot refrain from a guess at their future, particularly that of the new ones. I believe they will be obliged to make rather drastic changes in the traditions which have been on the whole very successful up to the present. There are not an indefinite number of able undergraduates and if these are allowed to choose they will congregate in certain places. An even distribution is unstable. There will probably not be enough to make all these universities up to present standards if they insist on doing the same things in the same way. But surely they need not. Our universities are too much concerned with words, written and spoken, too little with the ideas behind them and with things. Not every intelligent young man or woman wants to read for several hours every day. It is really rather an odd kink.

It is reasonable to suppose that by 1984 those who control the proposed new universities will have had time and experience enough to devise schemes which, while native to this country, will break away from the present tradition, admirable as it is for some. The problem is worse for the non-scientist. The scientist or doctor or engineer-to-be can feel that he is learning something he is actually going to use. The arts subjects, not tied by the need of being useful, somehow often fail to use their freedom to be exciting, which is the best excuse for non-utilitarian education. A society which is more aware of its vast possibilities, less content to do things the old way, will need people who have exercised their imaginations freely and also have been trained in the new ways of thought that are surely coming. I hope it will get them.

At a lower level, the problems of educating the less-bright for abundant leisure are exciting and call for even more drastic and revolutionary ideas. Few would claim that the 'secondary modern' is a success or even that one year more at school would improve it, but I have no experience in this field and cannot venture suggestions.

A NATION OF COMPUTER-KEEPERS?

by Sir Leon Bagrit

To adopt an all-embracing view of Britain's industrial position in 1984, taking account of the emergence of automation technology which, in practice, mainly means the application of scientific and advanced technological methods to almost every aspect of life, is plainly an impossible task. The best one can hope to do is to examine those of the trends which at this time appear important.

In particular, we must note what is happening in the U.S.A., technologically the most advanced country, and in the Soviet Union, which is making deliberate if cumbersome efforts to apply automation on a gigantic scale. In the rest of the world, apart from Europe, automation is unlikely to have the same urgent significance, and it seems that the gap in living standards between the technologically advanced and the backward ones will, unfortunately, tend to widen rather than to narrow. The only comfort is that the differential arises from the rapid advance of the industrialized countries, not from a decline in the standards of the underdeveloped countries.

In the United States automation is bursting the dam. The Americans have 17,000 computers installed or on order, costing some $6,000 million, and the indications are that, before 1984, they can expect to install computerized equipment to a value of $10,000 million *every year*. The effect of such massive investment, applied broadly throughout the commerce, the industry, the scientific institutions of a nation, must indeed be dramatic.

In Russia we observe errors in planning and execution which would not be tolerated in the industrialized West, but the scale of the efforts is such that, even with a proportion of failures, the rise in output must indeed be prodigious. If one considers that by 1984 more than *two million* graduates trained in disciplines applicable to automation will have been injected into their industrial complex, supported by large numbers of peasants released from work on the land by higher agricultural productivity, one cannot underestimate the challenge.

If Britain, too, takes automation seriously there is no doubt that a rise in wealth unprecedented in history will result, not from the replacement of man by the machine, but from the tightening of the 'slack' in the whole economic structure, by the removal of the inefficiency and wasted effort which is accepted today as normal. Speedy information, accurate and fast decision-making at all levels, rapid analysis and correction of activities, now feasible, will result in far more productive use of all our physical and mental resources.

Quite new concepts of social organization are inevitable. Take as a simple example the relationship of the smaller specialist manufacturer to a large producer who assembles components into a product. When computerized communications can be established between suppliers and retailers in a form which will feed back 'on-line' information of public demand directly to the manufacturer in a form which can be translated instantaneously into time-scales, quantities, and qualities required, we will approach a system which will be highly efficient and cheap, with small total stocks and little risk. The changes in demand will be immediately reflected in variations in the orders from suppliers at all stages.

Therefore, instead of large-scale manufacture requiring a vertically integrated organization, largely localized in one plant, in order to produce cheaply, we will find a number of efficient groupings arising which will achieve this very same result in spite of geographical separation. Costs will be cut without the need to re-site manufacturing facilities. For Britain this characteristic of automation could enable it to overcome the problem of its inertia of capital and make the nation highly competitive.

Thus automation does not necessarily lead to monolithic monopolies. By 1984 small manufacturing units, organized vertically by the integrated use of computerized communications, should be able to produce many manufactured goods capable of competing successfully with the largest organizations at home and overseas. Our national success will depend more upon the average level of efficiency of our individual manufacturers than upon the limited number of highly automated plants.

An outline of the degree of automation which many existing ndustries are likely to adopt can now be dimly discerned, but one must point to the inevitability of a large number of new products appearing which are unheard of today. In the course of the next fifty years the use of automation techniques in the manufacture of products known today may well be of secondary importance. More than half of all those employed in British industry today are producing goods which did not exist fifty years ago, and the rate of technological change is increasing.

By 1984, I would expect that the road system, the rail systems, and the air systems will be computer-controlled and integrated, and that hospitals, health services, libraries, universities, and even theological seminaries will be using computers and discovering new ways and means of managing their affairs and investigating the subjects in which they are interested.

Information analysis will open up fields of knowledge at present still hardly imagined. We already know what is possible by the use of these techniques in scientific and mathematical fields. We are beginning to see how these methods can be used in industry, in the analysis of literature and languages, and of military strategy, in translation, in medicine, in medical research and diagnosis. Even at this very early stage of automation we see a limitless vista before us.

Automation is not mainly a matter of replacing men, who will always be essential, but the demand will be for intelligent, educated, highly trained men and not for unskilled human machines. Today a large proportion of the human race is used simply as 'labour' to perform primitive, heavy, soul-destroying repetitive tasks, to use muscle for physical exertion, and eyes, ears, finger-tips simply as sensing devices to decide when to pull a lever or push a key. This is hardly a dignified use of the human being but it is tolerated because of necessity.

The glorification of 'work' for its own sake cannot persist into 1984. By that time it will be accepted that to use a human being in this way is inhuman; that a man has a right to demand that his senses and intellect are used to the fullest possible extent. His hours of productive activity will be adjusted to the extent necessary for society to function not only efficiently but humanely, for the humanist view of society should prevail. This process is in train even now, although, to rectify the present imbalance we must go through a period when the scientist and technologist advances in status at the expense of the humanist. With the growth of automation the need for a humanist view will not diminish but will indeed extend – adjusted by some knowledge of science as an essential part of a cultured education.

In viewing the next twenty years one should be aware of dangers. On the one hand, amid the violent changes which automation can bring about in the economic structure, reluctance to endow government with power to make effective adjustments could lead to major economic and social crises. That is more likely to be a grave danger in the U.S.A. than in Britain.

Here the risk of error is different, although no less dangerous, stemming not from too rapid changes, but from too slow. If we were able to live in isolation it might be satisfactory to adopt automation as slowly and as comfortably as we are doing now. Unfortunately, we are not insulated from the rest of mankind. On one side we have the gigantic productive resources of the United States, and on the other we see the build-up of the new industrial power of the U.S.S.R. Therefore Britain, like other European countries, is compelled to decide what actions must be taken to preserve, let alone improve, our position.

We have now had statements from both the Prime Minister and the Leader of the Opposition stressing the importance of technological change, of which automation is the core. Will we, by 1984, have gone far enough? So far, in many of our industries, Britain has been able to offset the greater mechanization of American industry by lower real wages. As automation is adopted in America on the broad industrial front, and the cost of labour plays a decreasing part in prices, the sale of American manufactured goods could increase quickly in relation to ours.

As for the Russians, they are prone to over-planning and will undoubtedly over-produce certain goods from time to time, and when that occurs they will consider it more economic to keep an automated plant running at full pressure, even if some of the surplus production has to be 'dumped' or exported at a loss.

How to maintain living standards for an increasing population on this small island in such circumstances, without adopting automation far more quickly and widely than we are doing, I do not know. The prospect would be dismal indeed if the present slow rate continued. At this time, to look at our likely position in 1984 with unqualified optimism is not easy.

WINNERS AND LOSERS IN THE RAT-RACE

by Barbara Wootton

Social changes are commonly induced by new technical developments; but, revolutions apart, they proceed at a much more sober pace. Twenty years hence the pattern of social life in Britain will not, I think, be dramatically different from what it is now. We shall not, for instance, be likely to find ourselves living in a classless society – in the sense of a society in which social intercourse and the choice of friends and spouses is unrestricted by class barriers. Twenty years hence an occasional duke (who has not turned himself into a commoner) may marry a dustman's daughter; but such an event will still be 'news'. And if one is invited to a meal at the house of a friend who is, say, a doctor or a lawyer, the presence in the party of a lorry driver or an office cleaner will still be quite startling.

At the same time there will be changes in the social pattern. Like the cities which it inhabits, with their office skyscrapers and inadequate housing, our society will have become increasingly top-heavy. The traditional pyramid, with a small upper class at the top, a somewhat larger middle class immediately below, and a much larger working class at the bottom, will have been squeezed and flattened. The top and the middle will be squashed into one another and both will be growing faster than the bottom. Eventually the end of this process may well be that the pyramid will be stood on its head, with a large body of professional and white collar workers in the upper classes and only a minority of manual workers below them. I do not think, however, that in twenty years' time we shall have got quite as far as that. The next stage is more likely to be one in which, in defiance of all geometrical propriety, the middle is situated at the top.

Moreover, the nature as well as the shape of the social hierarchy will be changed. Under the threat of automation the present occupational balance will certainly be quickly modified. Those flocks of typists, for example, who now flutter everywhere in and out of offices will soon be rare birds, in place of whose elegance we shall have only mechanical instruments. Again, in twenty years' time, even more than today, the passport to any kind of superior position will be the right to append certain letters to your name; and the opportunity to acquire such paper qualifications will certainly be more evenly spread than it is today. The present absurd division of children at, or even well before, the age of eleven into supposedly academic and non-academic types (for which, incidentally, there is no statutory authority) is already on its way out. By 1984 we may hope to see a fully comprehensive system; but whatever the form that this takes, education will, I fear, have become even more frankly and unashamedly a matter of successful certificate collection.

Still there will be some who cannot or will not succeed in this race. What will become of them? Some will follow the few remaining roads to financial success which are not barred by examination hurdles. They will build chains of restaurants out of an initial coffee stall or make fortunes by clever speculation. The scope for such individual enterprise may indeed be more restricted than in the past, and the dramatic life stories of the Nuffields and the Fortes may not be repeated. But even if the governments of the next twenty years are predominantly drawn from the Labour Party, I doubt if our way of life will have become so socialistic as to leave no way of escape for the occasional 'self-made'.

Others will take to the one profession for which absolutely no formal qualification is ever likely to be required – namely crime. In any increasingly competitive society I think we must expect rising figures of crime. The risk of criminality will be enhanced, too, if the present association between moral teaching and the Christian religion is perpetuated. In twenty years' time the number of people – particularly among the young – who find literal acceptance of the gospel story possible will be even smaller than it is today: and it will be even more urgently necessary that moral issues should be presented to these sceptics, in school and on the radio, in terms which involve no commitment to the supernatural. Indeed our present failure, in a scientific age, to disassociate morality from remarkably improbable dogmas must be counted as one of the most vulnerable features of contemporary society. If the next twenty years does not see general recognition of a purely secular morality, we must not be surprised to find that moral standards have been emptied away along with the Christian bath-water.

In any case we may expect – and welcome – significant changes in methods of dealing with those who continue to break the law. Already evidence is accumulating to show that existing methods of treating offenders are at best totally ineffective and at worst likely to do more harm than good. By 1984 we shall, I think, have been compelled squarely to face the issue of what ought to be the function of the criminal courts. In more and more instances it will no longer be possible to pretend that to punish the wicked and to diminish crime are identical, not alternative, courses. So the question will have to be faced: which shall we choose? And to that question there can, I think, eventually be only one answer. But radical indeed will be the change required in the mentality of lawyers – and indeed in that of much of the public also – before the criminal courts can be transformed into social agencies for the prevention of crime.

Not all the conventionally unsuccessful will, however, compensate themselves either by commercial enterprise or by dishonesty. Some will remain at the bottom of the social scale; and these, I expect, will continue to be drawn from the present two principal categories of second-class citizens – to wit, women and immigrants. These classes will continue to sweep railway carriages (if indeed any railways remain), to work as kitchen hands in hotels and restaurants, and generally to perform all the disagreeable, not very skilled tasks that have not already been automatized. But, though socially despised, these hewers of wood and drawers of water will doubtless earn considerably more money than they do today, so that in their off-duty appearance and in their possessions they will become less clearly distinguishable from their social superiors.

The picture that I have drawn is not a particularly attractive one; but its less agreeable features will probably be modified by increasingly generous provision for those who, like the elderly and the sick, are out of the race altogether. And we may confidently predict a much more liberal attitude on all questions of sexual morality. By 1984, the practice of adult homosexuality will surely have ceased to be criminal, and only the deeply religious will be shocked by pre-marital unchastity. Concern for a child's welfare will have finally swamped considerations of its parents' marital state, and divorce by consent (after how many years of marriage?) will be attainable legally, not, as now, only by subterfuge and perjury. Conceivably also, the sane and humane values of the many intelligent young people who have shown that they prefer Aldermaston-marching to rat-racing will have had a more profound influence upon our whole way of life than some of their faint-hearted elders can yet envisage.

North America

PATTERNS OF U.S. INDUSTRIAL DEVELOPMENT
by Professor George P. Baker
School of Business Administration, Harvard University

Changes of far-reaching importance will be occurring in U.S. industry during the next twenty years. While these changes will be more of an evolutionary than revolutionary nature, they will surely have a striking impact on the lives of men and women in the United States as well as on the nation's relations with the rest of the world.

To compare the future pattern meaningfully with the present, I shall give my best guesses as regards changes in the following dimensions: (1) products and industries; (2) marketing and production structure; (3) the general economic system; (4) management; (5) the philosophy and theory of business.

Products and industries. This dimension of change is the most apparent and visible to the public. Hence it will receive the most attention in the popular press.

The more dramatic changes in products will include such innovations as plastic houses, ultrasonic dishwashers, disposable clothing for factory workers and home handymen, electronic highways, and automatic trains. Also, new industries will capture the public fancy. In the south-west, and mid-west, water distribution will be a multibillion-dollar business; a host of new enterprises will become classified as space-industry firms; mining and farming are likely to be extended to ocean areas as well as land; self-instructional devices like programmed-learning and mobile-teaching units will provide a new aspect to education.

Dramatic increases in employment will be provided by these new kinds of business as well as by expansion in existing service, marketing, and research industries. By contrast, farming and manufacturing will account for a steadily declining proportion of total employment.

Marketing and production. How will goods and services be created ? How will they be brought to the public ? The changes that are coming in these patterns will affect our satisfactions not only as consumers but also as workers and investors.

Plants and offices will be integrated as never before by electronic data processing. Output information from the machines of production will register almost instantaneously in accounting, control, and warehouse inventory systems; data from sales outlets will register almost continuously in these systems, too. All this will keep the flow of goods from factory to store counter smooth and well organized.

At the consumer's end, retail centres will be larger and more attractive; people will do far more shopping at all-purpose stores where they can buy food, appliances, clothing, drugs, and furniture in one stop, and less shopping at specialized stores. Automatic merchandizing will account for a good many of our purchases. An important innovation will be the rise of contractual selling; that is, the renting or leasing of appliances, tools, cars, and perhaps even clothing. Thus, more emphasis will be on the *use* of goods and commodities, less on legal ownership of them.

The economic system. In thinking ahead about the U.S. economy of the 1970s and 1980s, most of the attention thus far has been given to working-force projections (over 100 million by 1984, probably) and gross-national-product forecasts (probably $1 *trillion* – 10^{12} – or more in 1984). However, such figures are not the whole story, or even the most important part of it.

For one thing, competition will be more 'wide open' than it has ever been before. This will come about, not because of changes in government regulation or antitrust policy, but because of the changing world scene. (What I say, therefore, will apply with equal force to industry in other nations of the free world.) Almost every business will be in competition with firms in distant geographical areas. Many factors will contribute to this trend, including increased speed in transporting products, new technologies, and revolutionary new packaging and handling systems made possible by higher volumes of shipments.

In addition, most firms will find themselves in competition with non-traditional and unexpected fields. For instance, we will find the leather industry in competition with the chemical industry, which will be marketing synthetic substitutes for leather; the textile industry will be subject to competition from the paper industry, which is succeeding in giving paper new properties; and some railroad coal haulers will be competing against extra-high-voltage electrical power transmission systems which will take advantage of new economies in their technology.

A second important change in the business pattern will be new forms of enterprise. In the handling of enormous new technological ventures in space and under the seas, joint ventures – teams of companies pooling their resources to accomplish a given objective – will be more common. On the international business scene, the transnational enterprise will assert itself; unlike present U.S. companies that operate branch and subsidiary operations overseas, the transnational firm will actually be owned by nationals of several different countries, with its stock sold on an international securities exchange and with its charter of incorporation perhaps coming from an international agency. This new business form might become a strong influence in the reduction of tariff walls and other nationalistic restrictions on international trade.

Management. Business patterns in 1984 will probably be altered significantly in still another dimension: management procedures and concepts. Decision making will be more rational than it is today. Experience will remain of great importance, but 'management by intuition' will be giving way rapidly to the use of analytical techniques and concepts for all phases of operations – for managing the human side of enterprise as well as the financial and physical. The amazing development of university management training, magazines as an educational tool, business research, and other trends will all hasten the maturation of this significant development. Just as in medicine the phrase 'think like a doctor' is common, so in management the phrase 'think like an administrator' will be often heard.

In addition, of course, computers will have great impact on management. In production scheduling, inventory control, marketing control, and research programming the 'black box' take-over will be very pronounced. In strategic planning (determining corporate policies and objectives, allocating resources to support plans, etc.) and in management control (translating strategic plans into budgets, assigning responsibilities for tasks and programmes, etc.) the computer will not be such a major factor. To pay its way, the computer must be given repetitive operations, and there must be marked needs for accuracy, speed, and processing of large quantities of data.

Business philosophy and theory. This last dimension of change in the industrial pattern is in some respects the most important of all. Our ideologies of business shift slowly and often imperceptibly, but when a change does set in, all of the economy feels it – from the largest manufacturing corporation to the smallest bakery shop.

How will thinking about business be different in 1984 ? In the first place, regulatory agencies will, I think, be more interested in the everyday realities of competition than in the artificial present-day formulas for 'market share' and 'market power' that plague business policy makers. This more empirical approach will surely release potentials for serving the consumer in the U.S.A. and abroad that are necessarily restricted today.

In the second place, and more important still, there will be a resurgence of appreciation of private enterprise. This will come about, not because of distrust of government (on the contrary, government should become more effective), but because of the changing industrial environment. The world of 1984, as I have already indicated, will be an extraordinarily complex, competitive, fast-moving world. It will be a world in which the consumer expects a lot of business – even a good deal more than he does today in nations of the West. He will be exceedingly demanding in his standards of service and quality, impatient when sudden shifts in his needs and desires are not swiftly met.

This being the case, private enterprise will be esteemed as never before. To be sure, public and quasi-public organizations will thrive in certain fields – for instance, in space and in various public services. But in most fields of industry they will be seen as a poor alternative to private enterprise. The independent corporation will be regarded as an agency that can plan, organize, and apply human and capital resources to meet the public's need with both a speed and an efficiency which no other form of organization can match.

FURTHER READING

1. Barach *et al.*, *1975*: *And the Changes to Come* (Harper 1962).
2. Anshen and Bach, *Management and Corporations 1985* (Harper 1960).
3. James Bright. 'Opportunity and Threat in Technological Change' (*Harvard Business Review*, November–December 1963).
4. Donald Kircher, 'Now the Transnational Enterprise' (*Harvard Business Review*, March–April 1964).
5. John Dearden, 'Can Management Information Be Automated?' (*Harvard Business Review*, March–April 1964).

CANADA: PLENTY OF ROOM FOR PEOPLE

by Dr K. F. Tupper

Vice-President (Scientific), National Research Council, Canada

Before trying to forecast twenty years ahead, one naturally looks back to see how much change has taken place in the twenty years past. One is always mindful of the possibility of a decade of very little change, such as 1929–39. My speculations are based on the assumption that things will change rapidly during the whole period 1964–84. I do not foresee any stagnant years.

By 1984 the population of Canada will be at least 35 million, compared with 19 million today. This increase will result from the combination of a steady natural increase and an excess of immigration over emigration. Because of its relatively high standard of living and its favourable political climate Canada will continue to attract immigrants from more crowded, more troubled, and less richly endowed areas of the world.

Nevertheless, in 1984 Canada will still be a relatively sparsely populated country, with immense natural resources. Its economy, as today, will be based on the exploitation of natural resources. We will be exporting wheat, pulp and paper, iron ore, nickel, and many other metals. The mining of uranium will have been resumed. The mining of gold will have ceased. By 1984 a number of rich mineral deposits, whose existence is unknown today, will have been discovered. Some large deposits, whose extent are now known, will have become economically recoverable.

But 'the hewing of wood and drawing of water' will not use the energies of all our people. To have something approaching full employment the Canada of 1984 will require a large secondary industry. While some of the problems of secondary industry will have been eased by the presence of a larger domestic market, many will remain, as the relative size of our domestic market will still be small. Manufacturers in certain other countries will continue to have much larger domestic markets than we have, and hence have far larger sales over which to spread the costs of research, design, development, and tooling. In spite of these fundamental difficulties, the sheer necessity of creating employment will make secondary industry inevitable.

There is still likely to be a small percentage of unemployed and the wits of labour leaders, industrialists, and politicians will be strained trying to find ways of increasing employment. Labour leaders will still be seeking shorter hours (at the same rate of pay); industrialists will want lower taxes so as to release profits for further capital expansion; political leaders will endeavour to establish new secondary industry by tariff adjustments.

Although we will have some of these present economic problems with us in 1984, the people of Canada will nevertheless be high on the scale of material well-being. They will be better fed, clothed, and housed than now or ever before in history.

The ratio of motor vehicles to people will probably have stabilized for the simple reason that cars will be so numerous that the increment of usefulness of additional vehicles will be substantially zero: lack of roads on which to drive them and parking lots and garages in which to leave them will make more cars virtually unwanted. But the business of maintaining and replacing cars will still mean a healthy motor-car industry.

By 1984 I expect that many big hydro-electric projects will have been completed. The Hamilton River in Labrador, the Columbia and the Peace in British Columbia, the Nelson in Manitoba will almost certainly have been developed. Some of the Quebec rivers flowing into James Bay, the Fraser in British Columbia, and possibly the Yukon in the Yukon Territory may be in the early stages of development.

Canada in 1984 will be a nation rich in energy resources. Nuclear power plants will be economic in Ontario. Coal and natural gas will provide power for the prairie provinces. Imported oil will probably provide the cheapest energy in the maritime provinces. Canada will be exporting electricity, oil, and natural gas.

The impact of science and technology is difficult to imagine. I see no radical changes in transportation, but a progressive increase in the use of aircraft. In communication it seems probable that the 1984 equivalent of today's television set can be connected at the wish of the owner to bring a wide variety of information. For instance, by dialling the public library one may be able to read any book while sitting in one's house, the printed page presented on the television screen. The blind, the lazy, and the illiterate can listen instead. The technology for vastly enhanced communication exists in some form today; the limitations are economic.

By 1984 Canadian agriculture will have become big business. The small and diversified farmers, who have been eking out a poor living, will have migrated to the towns. Land will be farmed efficiently, with machinery, in large blocks. The agricultural scientist will have found his place in the scheme of things. As a consequence more food will be produced with less labour.

In 1984 we will probably be worried by the instability of a system which causes a big operation to be more profitable than a small one, with the virtual disappearance of the small merchant, the small manufacturer, the small farmer. Although we will be alarmed that the big grow bigger and the small grow smaller and disappear, we will also realize that all our attempts to defeat this process represent subsidies of inefficiency. Not all of our economic problems will have been solved by 1984!

By 1984 a solution will have been found, I think, to Canada's serious problem of supporting two cultures and using two languages. I do not foresee what the solution will be.

Although the Canadians of 1984 will be well-off materially – in strong contrast to the people in some other countries (with and without comparable natural resources) – they will be becoming conscious of the fact that these material possessions have not brought them much happiness. There may well be a search in progress for other and better goals, but perhaps 1984 will be too early for that to be effective on any broad scale.

THE RISE OF THE METROPOLIS
by Dr L. V. Berkner

Graduate Research Center of the Southwest, Dallas

Dallas, Texas, 1984. – Our London editor has asked this correspondent for an assessment of North American development, with special reference to the past two decades (the post-Kennedy era). To evaluate the central elements of this advance in history suggests that we observe both the physical progress, and at the same time the developing mental attitudes and outlook of the populations.

Without doubt, these two decades of development have been dominated by the radical change in civilized status wrought by a rapidly advancing science, and the applications of that science through innovation (with its virile industry), to every aspect of man's ecology. The dominance of the traditional industry of necessity (food, clothing, shelter) has fallen almost completely before the science-based, *adaptive* industries derived from innovation. The ascendant stress on human stability has been man's need for continuous readaptation to an ever more rapidly changing environment.

The physical development of this resource-rich continent has been readily predictable from the rise of events since the mid-century. With new-found health from science, populations continue to soar, approaching 45 million in Mexico, 30 million in Canada and 300 million in the U.S.A. As everywhere, there is much talk, but no action, on the demographic problem in spite of obvious future dangers to society – a typical example of man's inability to adapt to changed conditions out of an inherited sense of morality that, in the past century, ought to have changed its algebraic sign.

Agriculture is now wholly industrialized, employing advanced concepts of mechanics, hydraulics, biology, genetics, chemistry and biochemistry. Basic production of food now directly occupies only three per cent of the population. In less than a half-century the continental emphasis has moved from agriculture to industry. This revolution has been especially noteworthy in Canada and Mexico.

The non-agrarian populations, now numbering 350 million, have migrated primarily to some 150 metropolitan areas. Each is a sprawling industrial and suburban complex, centred around one or more great graduate universities, which have been forced to provide the intellectual focus that guides the economic and cultural development of the city. Typically, this originally agrarian community – Dallas, Fort Worth, numbering less than a million at the mid-century – has been remoulded into a powerful educational, industrial, commercial, and financial centre now numbering nearly five millions (the size of New York just a few decades back). This story of metropolitan rise must be multiplied more than a hundred times.

The pattern of commerce is a complex network of revitalized railways (following the Japanese concepts of 1964), limited access super-highways, navigable canals and rivers, and airways that interconnect the several metropolitan complexes, employing highly automated terminal facilities. Fast communication networks and data-links now direct central operation of wholly automated and widely separated factory and distribution centres. Detailed manufacturing, inventory, and distribution control is exercised on an inter-continental scale. The introduction of the first rocket transports tends now to destroy completely the ancient concept of distance on our planet, substituting only the operational concept of time.

Consequently, the metropolis of one to ten million has become the dominant political unit, greatly superseding in influence the older county, state, or provincial units and governments. Nuclear energy is fast becoming the basic source of energy to provide power for the city, with petro-chemicals conserved for locomotion and for products of industry. Everywhere, water supply is critical with large-scale desalination and pollution control as a major metropolitan effort. Atmospheric pollution becomes ever more serious in the face of expensive measures to control it. City planning continued as negligible until about 1970, when incomprehensible congestion generated a sense of public outrage that could no longer be ignored. Then drastic measures involving more effective urban renewal and metro-transportation began to appear, leading to an unchoking of commerce within the metropolis.

In form, the city is tending to shape around the terminals of transport – airports, seaports, rail, and trucking centres – surrounded by industry and again by office and residential complexes. Efficient access to transport has become the key to metropolitan planning, with suburban areas acquiring both beauty and function. The universities and research centres are almost uniformly developing with easy access to the metropolitan hub. Of course, the older cities are slower to respond to these changes, though commercial competition is forcing more efficient functional patterns.

Underlying these great developments has been the extraordinary extension of advanced education to a major proportion of the population. This remarkable social upheaval can be seen in the rise of baccalaureate degrees, in the U.S. for example, during the twentieth century:

1900	28,000 annually
1920	50,000 annually
1940	200,000 annually
1960	450,000 annually
1980	21,000,000 annually

On one hand, this flood of populations to the universities has provided brainpower to develop and manage the innovative industry of our time. On the other hand, these numbers represent a whole new class of buying public, never before encountered in comparable numbers, whose tastes have profoundly modified the demands at the market place.

The explosion of education at the baccalaureate level has been matched by some 2,000,000 graduates annually at the two-year junior college level, and more than 4,500,000 annually at the secondary school (twelve-year) level. Education is by far the single largest economic effort.

The bottleneck of economic development has arisen primarily at the doctoral and post-doctoral level, where the most highly developed and creative brainpower commands the never-ending race between automation and innovation. In a sense, the level of unemployment in each metropolis is the measure of its success in joining this competition.

Superimposed on the older university system is the now major activity in each metropolis of *formal continuing education* for intellectual and community leaders that bids to extend through their lifetimes. With the rapid expansion of essential knowledge, failure to retread the mind leaves the individual hopelessly out of touch with the real world – the characters of power of his civilization. Consequently, the typical metropolis of 1984 is becoming the 'City of Intellect' with the revived and complex university system at the very core of its welfare. With the new metropolitan pattern, the theatre and the arts are enjoying a resurgence, thereby stimulating education through most needed critical approach to major problems of our time. There are, of course, tragic exceptions among the cities which are left educationally non-viable by stumbling leadership.

The absence of total conflict since 1945 has provided a plateau of stability for our remarkable continental development. This relative peace has been a surprise to some, yet the chauvinist, adventurer, and buccaneer has been under the powerful and certain restriction of the thermonuclear bomb and the powerful potentials of its delivery. In a sense, it has taken the ultimate weapon to deter the ultimate of war. Certainly international conflict continues, but only at a lesser and less positive level. Man, today, is uncertain how to police a system of justice, having been deprived of total war as the ultimate means. Consequently, international relations have assumed a highly experimental flavour as man gropes for dependable means of justice and its enforcement.

But man's frustration in this remarkable age runs even more deeply. Saddled with the *forms* of an ancient economy of scarcity which was his heritage for five millennia, he finds these forms, with all their deeply imbedded beliefs, largely inapplicable to his radically changed environment. No longer do the old rules work well; often they do not work at all, leaving populations confused and with a sense of helplessness and defeat.

Here the decline of liberal education during the past century has left a deep mark of failure. At the very time our civilization has seen the most remarkable evolution of all time – when for the first time poverty could easily be banished – man has been left without a widespread understanding of the rise and history of ideas. We find him widely ignorant of man's experience with ideas in the past, of the thought that is truly applicable to our time, or of the interpretation and impact of the new ideas of our day. The superficialities of the mainstream of twentieth-century literature leave man with little comprehension of the events which are swirling him up into the new environment. The ever-expanding philosophy, superimposed by scientific advance upon the older *ad hoc* concepts of human affairs, has yet to be widely grasped.

Therefore the ultimate stability of the present order remains open to question. Altogether new factors, not yet widely accepted, govern the stability of this new society, such as the balance of educational opportunity, the balance and extent of scientific research and exploration underlying innovation, and the delicate relation of effective management to human rights in the affluent society. A wide variety of such balances, often quite new to society – each balance with a fulcrum that is constantly moving – govern the future of community welfare. The continuance of a stable Western society emphasizing freedom of choice and natural selection of the most suitable course suggests an education and a literature pointed toward a broad public comprehension of the criteria on which the optimum choices can be based.

All of this suggests the rising urgency for a liberal education that penetrates the underlying philosophy of our new society. Without it, populations can be expected to behave like sheep, to follow the most plausible demagogue as he plays his flute down the road to disaster. Man's natural nostalgia for ancient form leaves him especially perplexed when his liberal education and literature have left him a century behind the times.

Finally, one cannot but comment on the growing imbalance between the 'have' and the 'have-not' populations. The science-based economies appear to thrive only with a certain minimum level of political stability. The major economic mechanisms of the great industrial nations seem to function only in such an atmosphere. Yet the requisite promise of stability is difficult to create among the yet largely uneducated populations. The extra-ordinary rise of the Mexican economy in the past three decades, preceded by the new Mexican standards of literacy and accompanied by political stability, is worthy of study. Quite aside from the moral question, the growing disparity between the 'haves' and the 'have-nots' seems destined ultimately to bring the affluent society down to ruin. Here, man faces his greatest challenge for analytical and objective study, and for pursuant effective action.

Latin America

SOIL AND SCHOOLS: THE BIG CHALLENGE

by Dr Tobias Lasser

Director of the Institute of Botany, Caracas, Venezuela

If one wishes to make a prognosis of Latin America's potentialities, from whichever angle it is viewed, the first thing which must engage our attention is the very accelerated growth of its population, common denominator of all the basic problems that will affect the development of this continent. Today the population of Latin America is estimated at some 220 million inhabitants. With such a growth rate as is indicated statistically, this population will rise to 370 million by 1984, which will exceed North America's population by nearly 100 million.

The advances during the last two decades in hygiene and sanitation in many Latin American countries have reduced the death rate in such a manner that their population is conspicuous by the great number of young people which comprise it. For example, 89·2 per cent of Venezuelans reach the age of 15 years, and 54 per cent of its population is made up of people under 19 years of age. At this rate of growth, the future of adequate education for this growing multitude of young people is hindered, not only because of lack of facilities, but also because of the need for experienced men, who have always been scarce, to open and manage new developments and educational enterprises. This unbalanced condition between the productive classes and the inactive classes will deeply affect the economic development.

The impact of this teeming population on the landscape will be felt most strongly, and will leave the deepest impression, in the tropical area of Latin America.

From a total of 2,240 million hectares, 364 million hectares are available for agricultural uses, distributed in different types of lands according to their food-producing capacity. This corresponds to less than 2 hectares *per capita*. Of this grand total, forests extend over 890 million hectares, of which 561 million are inaccessible, leaving a remnant of useful forests, either in production or not, with an area of 329 million hectares. The area of productive forest, then, is one and a half hectares per inhabitant.

By 1984 the quota of agricultural and forest land is expected to diminish respectively to less than one hectare per inhabitant. This makes 1984 a crucial time in Latin America's development if it is agreed that in the tropics one hectare of arable land is the minimum of living space from which a person may enjoy some material comfort, and that more or less 50 per cent of its population devote themselves to agricultural activities.

The development of any region is determined by physical as well as cultural factors. Among the former, the outstanding factor is the soil. It is well to note that industrial development, the supreme ambition of the Latin American countries, must be preceded by agricultural development, in order that the market capacity of the hinterland guarantees the process of industrialization. Of the cultural factors, education is the most noteworthy, as the means of guiding the new generations so that they may contribute to general progress.

Soil and land use. The troubles of Tropical America are often blamed on the 'imperialist' countries, which exploit their natural resources, and on the low prices of the raw materials and of the agricultural products that are exported, in contrast with the high prices of imported products. This is only one aspect of the truth. The other explanation is rooted in its soils. The fragile agricultural soils of the tropics are constantly being destroyed. Soil bacteria, under the stimulus of tropical heat, are active all through the year, decomposing the humus complex, while in the temperate regions the soil is preserved for several months during the year because of lower temperature conditions which retard bacterial activity. This helps to explain the more progressive state in the temperate zones.

When Columbus arrived on the continent, he found the Indians practising one of the most rudimentary agricultural systems: shifting agriculture. Soils become exhausted after a few crops; for this reason they abandoned them for new fields, which were in turn cleared, burned, and cultivated. This system has neither been eliminated nor replaced by a stable agriculture. Instead, it has been increased and is often practised on steep slopes, thus making the soil more quickly exhausted, and causing deterioration in the catchment basins. This system of agriculture is one of the reasons for the low income of the farmers in Tropical America. Another factor is that large land estates, comprising about 50 per cent of agricultural lands, are devoted to extensive cultivation of one crop – such as coffee, cocoa, bananas, sugar cane, and cotton – destined for export and subject to market fluctuations.

In order to increase agricultural production, agrarian reform has been recommended, but that is not only a matter of solving the social and economical problems. It is largely a problem of making rational use of soils: land classification, contour farming, strip cropping, crop rotation, and terracing. Moreover, productive agriculture depends on mechanization, irrigation, fertilizers, and pesticides in sufficient quantities, the establishment of farm cooperatives, and the founding of experimental stations to obtain seeds of high-yielding quality. Moreover capital must be available to finance these enterprises with long-term, low-interest loans. Unfortunately the Latin American mind is not adapted to such enterprises which require a long period for their realization. Here, economic thought demands quick profits from investments.

Education. Illiteracy is one of the major hindrances in the development of Latin America. The percentage varies for each country but it may be said that, even though great efforts have been made to reduce it, approximately 50 per cent of the population is illiterate, and moreover there are millions of children of school age for whom thousands of schools must be built, and thousands of teachers prepared. In Venezuela in the last five years illiteracy has been reduced to 20 per cent.

With the exception of Mexico, where the rural educational system is well developed, rural teaching in all other Latin American nations has started without a definite orientation.

The Latin American school system is adapted neither to our needs nor to the times in which we live. In the elementary schools *instruction* is given, to the neglect of moulding character, responsibility, good manners, or the spirit of collaboration. This same situation prevails in high schools, where students are prepared to go on to study in the universities, although a high percentage do not obtain a diploma.

The situation in the technical colleges is contradictory, because of the contrast that exists between the scarce numbers of technical students and those of the universities, when it should be the other way round. Of course the students prefer the universities to the technical colleges because of the prestige derived from a university diploma, as well as the better salaries after graduating. But the needs of Tropical American countries and their state of development require a great number of technicians.

The efficiency of the schools of medicine and engineering in the Latin American universities is evidence that these universities may be as successful as their European and American counterparts. Two factors are responsible for their advantage: (1) learning by *doing*; and (2) the essential sense of responsibility. Physicians and engineers who graduate from these universities will not succeed in their careers if they allow their patients to die or their bridges to collapse.

In order to develop the other schools we must take into account, besides these two factors, a system of selecting those students who may take advantage of a university education, as well as appropriate regulations for the teaching function and students' activities. Some universities become centres of great political ferment and countless students dedicate themselves to such activities, so that the true, constructive aims of university life are contaminated.

The prospect for Latin America in 1984 is therefore not very satisfactory, because of the dwindling of its natural resources and an inadequate educational system on the one hand, and the accelerated growth of population on the other.

A nationalism impregnated with extremist ideas, growing signs of family disintegration, social tension and frustrations, combined with a high unemployment index, will be a challenge to the leaders in these countries. Thus if the leaders do not succeed in making the rate of economic development exceed the rate of the population growth and in bringing about a profound reform in the educational system, they will find themselves in much the same position as some bullfighters who, in the presence of excited and aggressive bulls, do not know what to do with them.

IN PLACE OF FEUDALISM

by Professor Abelardo Villegas

Pan-American Institute of Geography and History, Mexico

No radical transformation of Latin American society can be expected in so short a time as twenty years. Many South American countries have not changed substantially since colonial days, and it is almost futile to hope that they will do so by 1984. That is not to say no elements exist which may bring about a change but, in the ultimate, it will depend upon man's desire for freedom and his capacity for suffering; upon his rebelliousness and his resignation. There have been cases in which societies have been quickly transformed at turning points in their history; others in which the people have shown an incredible acceptance of a quite exceptional series of catastrophes.

The social problem in Latin America, the most important problem of all, will be no nearer solution in twenty years' time than it is today. The expected increase in population is not excessive, if we consider the size of the continent and its potential resources; it is, however, excessive in view of the methods of government and the systems of production employed. That is to say, there is a contradiction in a society which increases very rapidly and which, at the same time, retains a feudal system of land ownership. If, therefore, the new population is to feed itself, clothe itself, be educated, and, in general, rise above the poverty in which these anachronistic forms of economy retain it, it must become more flexible. At the same time, the privileges of particular social classes or groups must be eliminated. With the exception of a few countries which have started to dismantle feudalism (such as Mexico, Argentina, Brazil, Chile, and Cuba) the landowning class, the big planters, predominate and influence both politics and education. It is this class which will be most affected during the next twenty years: it will have to resist the pressures of the needy masses or be overwhelmed by them.

In either case, the political consequence will be such that no democracies, in the conventional meaning of the term, can arise. To survive, feudalism will continue, as always, to support and lead strong or dictatorial governments which retain the landowner's privileges. The privileged military and ecclesiastical groups will remain. On the other hand, if popular revolutions succeed, proclaiming agricultural reform, strong or dictatorial governments will have to be set up, to safeguard the revolutions and suppress counter-revolutionary groups – as has occurred in Mexico, Bolivia, and now Cuba.

In short, the next twenty years will be a period of transition, of unrest and revolution, and no democracy of the classical type can flourish in such cases, with its effective suffrage, stability of power, regular elections, and so forth.

As for industrialization and development of a capitalist class following the extinction of feudalism, a situation of a similar type will arise in all except the out-and-out Socialist countries: competition between Latin American capitalism and that of other countries – particularly North America. In this competition the relatively weak Latin American interests will be able to survive only with help from their governments. The price paid for such aid will be state intervention in the private sector of the economy and, in many cases, the nationalization of the basic industries. In such an event, the workers will, if organized, be in a strong position to assert their rights.

If, on the other hand, home-grown capitalism does not prosper, enterprising industrialists from North America and elsewhere will supervene. The workers in our countries will not be able to claim their rights because the state will side with the overseas investors and will be managed by them. Moreover, such an outcome will not necessarily mean that our countries will become industrialized; it may instead simply favour the expansion of industry in the richer countries themselves.

Obviously, the achievement of agricultural reform, and the consequent industrialization, depend to a great extent upon world events and especially upon the development of the 'cold war'. It is essential that there should be a reduction in international tension if the Latin American countries are to start or complete a radical transformation of their society. When we consider that the 'cold war' has been going on for about fourteen years, we need not be surprised to find it a continuing issue for the next twenty. We have already seen the formation of a third group of nations alien to both 'East' and 'West' – a group of nations which, regardless of their political and economic systems, refuse to take sides in the 'cold war'. If the Latin American countries bind their destinies tightly to either the capitalist or the communist groups, their national interests will be subordinated to those of their principal allies. On the other hand, it is probable that, if there is no outbreak of nuclear war (and it would be futile to speak of any future without that assumption) the uncommitted countries will increase in number and influence.

There will thus be, in the next twenty years, a strong tendency on the part of the Latin American countries towards emancipation from the feudal and colonial condition, and towards entry into the group of uncommitted nations. This tendency will be the same in both non-socialist and socialist countries.

In conclusion, it is extremely unlikely that the countries of Latin America will become wholly converted to communism, as we have seen from events in Cuba. There are groups inside and outside Latin America which are most anxious that there shall be no repetition of the Cuban episode, and they will use their great influence and power to prevent it. Nevertheless, they will be handicapped by the contradiction I mentioned at the beginning of this article – that between the increase in population and the increase in wealth. For this reason I believe that the Latin American renaissance will trace a number of paths intermediate between absolute socialism and capitalism.

A CONTINENT OUT OF DATE

by Professor Josué de Castro

Formerly Brazilian Ambassador to the U.N. (Geneva)

Nothing is more risky or more uncertain, in my opinion, than a projection of the historical process, because the interaction of a great number of factors, through countless variations, may completely alter the foreseeable picture of social transformation. But I recognize the need for it and its possible usefulness in a world undergoing such a rapid transformation. In trying to minimize the probabilities of error in such a prognosis, we may consciously adopt two approaches: (1) mathematical projection of existing trends, which would give us a strictly accurate picture of the real world in the future only if civilization could be treated in the same way as the world of physics: (2) speculation to conceive an idealized picture of the future, not of a real world, but of a possible world which could be reached by transition from the real world.

The map of Latin America shows today the following predominant features. Its territory covers an area of 8·9 million square miles (16 per cent of the total inhabited lands), with approximately 220 million inhabitants (7 per cent of world population). Twenty sovereign states and some colonial territories constitute the political mosaic of this vast region, which extends from the southern borders of the U.S.A. almost down to the Antarctic. Spread over this territory we find vast resources in oil and the most varied types of minerals. The resources in land suitable for agriculture are also enormous and for the most part unexploited. Thus, Latin America appears as a considerably vaster and potentially richer region than North America, but the social and economic conditions of her peoples are much more backward.

As a whole, Latin America is one of the great underdeveloped areas of the world, showing in her social patterns all the characteristics of underdevelopment: extremely low income, high birth and death rates, alarming indices of illiteracy (around 70 per cent), high incidence of endemic disease, and widespread malnutrition affecting two thirds of the population. The *per-capita* income is around $350 – one third of that of Western Europe and one eighth of that of the United States. The disparities of income levels are alarming, not only between different countries or areas of the same country, but also between different social strata. In three Latin American countries alone – Brazil, Argentina, and Mexico – is concentrated two thirds of the total production of the continent. 10 per cent of the Latin American population enjoy 80 per cent of the total wealth of the continent, and half of the remaining 90 per cent live completely outside the economic process, with a practically non-existent income or means of obtaining manufactured goods. The feudal agrarian system reigning in nearly all Latin America preserves this inequality, since only an insignificant minority possess land, whereas the majority live as serfs of the great feudal landlords. In Venezuela, only 3 per cent of the population own 90 per cent of the land, and in Brazil 2 per cent of the landowners concentrate in their large estates more than 50 per cent of the whole cultivated land of the country.

The greatest part of the Latin American population still draws its income from the primary sector of production (agriculture and mining) and particularly from the production, by archaic agricultural methods, of exportable commodities such as coffee, sugar, and tobacco, which account for the bulk of the Latin American export earnings. The structural weakness of this economic system does not favour a development of the region in keeping with its material possibilities and with the increasing needs of its exploding population.

The result is a picture of dark misery, covering today nearly the whole of the 'continent of plenty' found by the Spanish *conquistadores*. It represents an extensive portion of the world's geography of hunger, with roughly 100 million human beings short of food, poorly clothed, worse housed, illiterate, and, at the same time, reproducing at a high rate. Nor, if we simply project the economic trends manifest in the region, can any great changes be foreseen in the next twenty years which could fundamentally alter the picture. Slow economic growth will hardly do more than keep pace with the growth in population.

The incapacity shown up to now by Latin America to enlarge her present very limited range of exports speaks against the possibility of increasing imports of industrial equipment. Discrimination against Latin American products and the fall in world commodity prices more than cancel out all the loans and financial assistance provided by the great powers and international organizations. The pittance spared by Latin America for education does not presage the great educational leap which could change the cultural patterns of the region.

Health and food are consumer goods that a people can acquire only in accordance with its purchasing power. The chances for Latin America to free herself from disease and hunger, without adequate resources, are not favourable. Thus, if we simply extrapolate from present facts, we cannot hold out much hope for anything beyond the humble situation of being the leading area of the underdeveloped world, somewhere ahead of the African and Asian countries which, for many reasons, are still further behind in their development process.

I refuse to believe that this is the correct forecast. If we examine more closely the social reality of Latin America, and try to break through the surface of apparent facts, we see that the forces of social revolution are gathering, which will inevitably sweep, in the coming years, over the whole continent. The portrait of Latin America in 1984 appears quite different if we take that into account.

When the United States became aware of this impending continental revolution, it proposed, in August 1961, in Punta del Este, the operation called Alliance for Progress, a policy which accepted in theory, as a basic requirement of the development plans of the region, the urgent need for total change of the dominant social structure, hence the need for a real social revolution. In practice, however, the effect has been to prevent such reform. Thus our conviction is renewed that only social revolution can really solve the problems of the people. The subsequent development of the now insignificant rural market and the increased productivity in raw materials and food will bring about a parallel expansion of industry.

Latin America is one of the regions which could benefit most from world-wide disarmament and the conversion of the world economy. In spite of all domestic and external obstacles to development, there are some countries that are close to the level of economic 'take-off': Brazil, Mexico, and Argentina. Their higher technological and cultural levels, their wider entrepreneurial experience, and the existing industrial nuclei offer attractions for the investment capital that would be made available by disarmament. Given these conditions, then, at least three Latin American countries will be able to raise themselves above the barrier of underdevelopment between now and 1984. In other countries, expansion will proceed at a pace that will be relatively slower; yet, in my view, it will be faster than would be predicted by classical economists, who interpret the economic process as simple accounting procedure and fail to take into consideration the creative power that a people can generate at certain moments of history.

Africa

OBSTACLES AND OPPORTUNITIES

by Dr F. T. Sai

Regional Office, Food and Agriculture Organization, Accra

Africa, for a long time referred to as the 'dark continent', has come to take its place in world affairs during the last decade to an extent never considered possible twenty years ago. This change has occurred largely because of the tempo of African political development. If the political forces of Africa are properly directed, then the ground will be prepared for an unprecedented rate of scientific, technological, social, and economic development of almost all parts of the continent. The recently established Organization of African Unity is a step in the right direction. In its constitution and aims there is the potential for assisting in the solution of the many interterritorial and interregional difficulties. It will assist in the establishment of stable and responsible governments, and there is enough to indicate that within a few years a truly closely knit 'African Community' will have emerged.

Such a development is required to pave the way for a rational industrial development and the marketing of both primary and industrial products. It will also make for cooperation and coordination of research activities, education and training, and the attack on endemic diseases. Practically, the entire future of African development will be gloomy indeed if some kind of political and economic *rapprochement* between the African states cannot be guaranteed. I am optimistic that this will be forthcoming. In what follows, the problems and opportunities in the fields of human resources, health, food and nutrition, and energy resources are viewed over a score of years.

Human resources. The most pressing problem which is at once a challenge and an opportunity is the growth of the population with the attendant need to develop to the fullest the human resources. The population of Africa was estimated by the United Nations at 261 million in 1961 (*Demographic Yearbook*, U.N.). A projected low figure of 341 millions and a high of 428 millions are given for the year 1985 (*The Future Growth of World Population*, U.N.). Even if the mid-projection of 364 million (a figure likely to prove too low) is accepted for 1984, this still means a population increase of 50 per cent. Though this in itself does not pose any problem of over-population, the non-productive fraction will still be almost 50 per cent of the population. The development of these human resources must antedate any real progress on the continent.

Crash programmes for both mass adult and formal education are to be implemented and expanded. The question of lack of trained teachers will not seriously hinder success because new educational tools such as programmed teaching and television will be extensively employed. One of the major research activities in the next decade or more will be toward the evolution of teaching methods and teaching aids and especially the production of science apparatus for teaching children who have to bridge the gap between the Stone Age and the Atomic Age in a lifetime. A major activity all over Africa will be the training of the new teacher to cope with this problem.

At present countries like Malawi (formerly Nyasaland) and Ethiopia (according to F. Harbinson, *Scientific American*, September 1963) have only between 1 and 2 per cent of their children of secondary-school age at school. Ghana has about 25 per cent, and most of the African countries south of the Sahara lie in between these two. The next twenty years will witness marked increases in these figures with almost all countries reaching a 25-per-cent minimum. The development of universities, at present on a national basis, will be accelerated and regionally oriented to produce both the scientists and technologists for the numerous development projects.

Energy and power. At present the problem of energy for development appears to be almost insoluble in many African countries. The heavy dependence on petroleum products does not help an already difficult foreign exchange situation. Nuclear energy, in spite of optimistic forecasts in the past, will not make much contribution in Africa because the outlay required in trained men and money will not be available in twenty years. Hydroelectric power will be developed wherever possible. An intensive effort to discover more fuel sources, especially in the Sahara, is likely to yield petroleum products and natural gas in such quantities as to make a material contribution to the fuel needs of many states south of the Sahara. Proper supplies of energy will make for better intra-Africa communications. Transcontinental roads will not become major commercial routes by 1984 but a start will have been made.

Food and nutrition. Food for the African population is one of the most challenging problems today. In most African countries the overall yearly intake of calories falls below the theoretical requirements. In many, pre-harvest hunger is a yearly phenomenon and in years of drought, hurricane, or locust invasion actual famine conditions exist. Children in many areas are particularly badly off and receive 20-50 per cent fewer calories than they would require. Protein-rich foods, such as meat, fish, milk, poultry, and even the vegetable ones such as peas, beans, and groundnuts are in short supply. Again the children fare worse than the adults, and protein-calorie deficiency is the common lot of the African toddler today. Localized deficiencies of riboflavin, vitamin C, and vitamin A are found in the drier areas.

The next twenty years will witness an agricultural revolution on the continent. Attempts will be made on an international level to stop the spread of the Sahara and to introduce better systems of land use. Mechanization (especially following the introduction of the 1 to 2 horse-power tractor), seed selection, and the proper application of fertilizers will make for at least a twofold increase in the yield of staples. Vacuum drying, with and without prior freezing, will be a major method of processing perishable foods. Strategically distributed silos and low-cost packaging will both assist to bring food to the consumer throughout the year. Both the calorie supply as well as the supply of vitamins will become adequate.

On the other hand, the problems of supply of protein-rich foods will not be satisfactorily resolved except in the case of foods for weanlings. Legumes and the proteins obtained from bacterial de-waxing of petroleum products will be used for producing very low-cost weaning foods. Beef and milk will continue to make negligible contributions to the diets of the equatorial and tropical masses. Problems such as breeding the right stock, disease resistance, and disease control are unlikely to be solved within twenty years. But the protection and controlled use of wild life for food is likely to yield major sources of animal protein in some East African countries. Fish and poultry development will help in certain specific areas only.

In general terms, then, food production and distribution would become sufficiently satisfactory to provide the population with its full calorie requirements. Special attention to the needs of the toddler will yield a food rich in both calories and proteins, but the juicy steak, fillet of fish, and milk are unlikely to reach the 'average' African table by 1984.

Health. Enough is known at present to bring most of the important diseases of Africa under control. Malaria will be tackled on a continental scale. The older chlorinated hydro-carbons will continue as the major insecticides but newer derivatives to which insects will only slowly become resistant are likely to emerge. Organo-phosphorus compounds, e.g. malathion, dichlorvos fenthion (*W.H.O. Chronicle*, Vol. 17, No. 10), now being tested by W.H.O., are likely to be used increasingly on a short-term basis to support the older drugs. Spraying combined with mass prophylaxis using one of the 'depot' or slow-release antimalarial drugs now under test will completely break the cycle of transmission and bring malaria under control.

Most countries will deliberately choose an extensive rather than an intensive kind of health care and concentrate on the production of large numbers of auxiliaries to support a small band of doctors. This force will then be mobilized for a successful assault on the major endemic diseases such as yaws, leprosy, trypanosomiasis, and tuberculosis.

The helminths (worms) pose a different problem. Hookworm and ascaris, due largely to faulty sanitation, will disappear from the towns but will still remain a problem in the rural areas. The insect-born filarial worms such as onchocerciasis (river blind-ness) and elephantiasis will receive their deserved attention only during the latter part of the period under consideration. The increasing use of irrigation and multi-purpose dams in agriculture will lead to an initial increase in bilharziasis (schistoso-miasis) in many areas; but by 1984 potent and non-toxic molluscicides for killing the snails that transmit the disease should have been found and the stage set for a solution. Finally, major improvements in the health field are likely to follow in the wake of the developmental projects such as industrialization, roads, housing, and large-scale agriculture. The infant mortality rate, at present 100–300 per 1,000, is likely to be down to 50 or less per 1,000, with a consequent marked increase in the expec-tation of life.

Conclusion. My view of Africa 1984 is therefore optimistic. This springs from the fact that the major problems facing the continent can be solved if knowledge already available is widely applied. A greater coordination and cooperation is required of the African states. Rational development and siting of industries can only be achieved on a regional or continental basis. Efforts at research and training will also be more progressive if tackled at an interterritorial level. The present iniquities inherent in world trade, which tends to make the primary producing countries even poorer, will be removed only if a united Africa encourages inter-African trade and exerts its full force on the world market. This can only be achieved if political stability, cooperation, and coordination are assured – as I think they will be.

ROOM FOR FAR MORE PEOPLE

by Robert Gardiner

Executive Secretary, U.N. Economic Commission for Africa, Addis Ababa

Since authors in this series are asked to base their contributions on the facts of current developments, I shall start with the realities of 1964 and the likely trends in the coming two decades.

The Africa of today is a continent characterized by two main features – poverty and fragmentation. Some sectors have been developed quite highly, especially mining and export agriculture; since, however, the relationship has been essentially one of providing metropolitan countries with primary products, in return for manufactures, much of the economy has remained very backward. Large areas of Africa show as yet few of the normal services of the twentieth century, such as health and education.

Secondly, we have to live with the fact that the colonial powers divided the continent according to their own political needs. Frontiers run through homogeneous tribal groups and separate those who speak the same language, as well as cutting up natural economic units. The consequences are especially noticeable in West Africa, where there are more than a score of small countries, many of which can only survive with difficulty as separate economies.

Governments are now consciously trying to correct these two basic weaknesses. In the first place, they put economic development above almost every other objective. Secondly, there is a strong and growing trend towards political and economic unity. The Economic Commission for Africa, for example, has in its programme of work for 1964 concrete steps towards an African common market and a payments union, and work is in hand for the coordination of industrial development plans for East and Central Africa, West Africa, and North Africa respectively; an African Development Bank has already been established.

How successful will these policies be by 1984? Let us start with the influence that can most easily be predicted – the continent's population. The growth of population is likely to accelerate. At the moment it is between 2 and $2\frac{1}{2}$ per cent *per annum*; if the death rate continues to fall, but the birth rate remains unchanged, the population will grow over the next twenty years at a rate of nearly 3 per cent a year and will reach about 400 millions by 1984.

There is room for far more people in Africa. Taken as a whole, it is not beset by the problem of excess population, except for one or two areas, particularly the Nile Valley. But the growth of population does pose the problem of how to find the capital for a fast enough economic development. Already, it is hard to provide adequate social services, and above all to find productive employment for the growing labour force.

One would be more optimistic about an adequate pace of

development if exports were more buoyant. Most projections, however, anticipate a growth of primary product sales at only moderate rates, with a major exception – the growing flow of petroleum from under the Sahara.

What does this imply for 1984? If we assume, as we must, that Africa will solve her economic problems, she will necessarily be much more self-sufficient. There will be a moderate degree of industrialization by then, including a number of steel mills. Associated with this, educational levels will be much higher; there will be universal primary education (this has already been almost achieved in several countries), but the biggest advance will be the creation of many new technical colleges, universities, and research institutes.

It is not easy for countries with the current low levels of technical knowledge to diversify their economies. The next two decades will be periods of strain, with setbacks from time to time. And one cannot expect these strains to have disappeared by 1984 – particularly if unemployment has not been substantially absorbed by then.

One must anticipate that by 1984 the pressure for change will have produced political forms adapted to the African scene. The institutions of many, if not most, African countries will be different from those of either Western Europe or the Soviet bloc. The more the economic climate has improved in the meantime (and this depends very much on the establishment of regular flows of aid), the less radical the political transformation is likely to be.

One type of change which can be anticipated is a higher degree of cooperation, including a number of customs unions and federations, perhaps even a big federation covering the bulk of the continent. The necessary degree of industrialization implies this. There will be a network of communications, including almost certainly a continental rail system, and good trunk roads making it possible to drive comfortably across the Sahara and through tropical jungle.

There remains the problem of South Africa. That seems to be a case where irresistible forces are meeting immovable obstacles. At some point the forces of change will win, but our understanding of social change is not sufficiently precise to enable us to say with certainty that this will be accomplished by 1984. It depends in part on the attitude of other countries, especially the United Kingdom. What is reasonably certain, however, is that African governments will by then rule in the whole of the rest of the continent, including countries which are not yet independent.

Asia

THREE FIFTHS OF MANKIND

by Dato Sir Alexander Oppenheim
Vice-Chancellor, University of Malaya

Science is a common heritage to all mankind, though the leading role in the history of its development has been played by different races at different times. Once it was the Greeks, at another time the Islamic people, then the Europeans, and now the Americans and Russians. By the year 1984 modern science will have brought dramatic changes to the livelihood of many Asian people, some of whom are still living under conditions similar to those prevailing during the days of their ancestors a few thousand years ago.

Many more scientists will be produced by universities in Asia, and at the same time more Asian scientists trained abroad will return to their homeland. It is impossible to predict any forthcoming contributions of great significance to the fundamental knowledge of pure science emerging from the minds of scientists in Asia within the next two decades. At any rate it is unlikely that Asia will seriously challenge the leadership of Europe and America, although the gap between them will become narrower. One reason is that scientifically backward countries today generally concentrate on the applied sciences and technology, paying less attention to research into the more fundamental aspects of pure science.

It will be in the fields of applied science and technology that the greatest progress will be made in Asia. By 1984 industrialization will have taken place in many countries, including China, India, and Malaysia. These countries will require a much shorter time to become industrialized than that which was taken by Europe and North America in the past, they being able to take advantage of the experience gained by their predecessors. Reactors will be used in many power stations and electronic computers in many organizations. Electronic diagnostic equipment will probably be developed and used in hospitals in some countries, such as Japan. Higher-yield and better-quality natural rubber will continue to compete with synthetic. Some Asian countries such as Japan and China will produce their own motor vehicles in large quantities, while others like India and Malaysia will assemble sufficient motor vehicles to meet the demands of their home markets. Japan will become one of the pioneers in the production of turbine-motor engines. By the year 1984 Asia will not only be very close behind Europe and America in the applied sciences and technology but it will also become their greatest competitor in the world supply of manufactured goods and scientific equipment.

However, it is not merely in the fields of science and technology that we are likely to see startling changes in Asia. Far more important will be the human problems which must accompany advances in science and technology. It is difficult today to make generalizations about changes in the population structure of Asia because Asia's societies and cultural groups are so diversified. But one thing seems certain: by 1984 the population of Asia will be over two and a half billion, nearly twice the present number; out of every five persons in the world, three will be Asians. Most of the present Asian population is young and eager, so that little decline in the present rate of growth can be hoped for save in so far as Malthusian checks on human foolishness (or wisdom) can take control. All facets of Asian life will reflect this huge increase in population which poses the severest challenge to the scientific and social skills of man in the decades to come.

Unfortunately pressure on existing agricultural land is unlikely to be relieved, given the limited space now available. Only a few fortunate Asian nations with adequate capital or organizational discipline will be able to convert such harsh environments as the Malayan jungle or the Yunnan scraplands to food production. Scientific control of water and of crops will certainly improve yields; sophisticated techniques of food production such as hydroponic farms and protein extraction from vegetable or algal raw materials are going to be highly developed. Yet technical advances may barely keep pace with increasing numbers, and *per capita* levels of nutrition, health, and productivity may well decline, as has already happened in Java. Communes or kibbutzim, the prototype instruments of authoritarian régimes today, will become more attractive. At the same time, peasant production can hardly disappear.

The Asian city will display the clearest effects of population pressures. By 1984, most of the world's greatest populated cities will be in Asia, culminating in giant conurbations against which modern Tokyo would seem small. However, only a handful will incorporate planning or urban-renewal concepts of the 1960s, as most will be overworked just to provide essential health, power, and food services for the rising numbers of migrants and indigenous dwellers. Some Asian cities will, no doubt, build prestige housing, at planned densities of up to 4,000 people per acre. Like municipal projects in Hong Kong today, these will probably take the form of multi-storey blocks, each embodying a large proportion of prefabricated elements, which provide no more than the barest minimum of floor space per family. The lucky minority occupying these ferro-concrete cliffs will at least enjoy standards of living far above those forced into decaying buildings or shanty towns that, as in Calcutta today, will spread for miles around the urban core. And the inhabitants of these conurbations will enjoy, as in the West, the delights of auto-intoxication, for those who have tasted the nectar of speed will not forego the disadvantages the automobile is known to bring.

In these cities, the contrast between an occupational or professional élite and an economically depressed proletariat will be sharpest. Yet in response to public opinion, however muted, provision for bridging the gap can be expected. One such bridge will be the Asian university. As a whole, most universities will focus their energies on the utilitarian aims of training a professional cadre, if only to cope with the severe problems of an expanding population. Yet we can also hope for major contributions to basic and applied knowledge, if only because the reservoir of human talent feeding Asian universities is so large. These universities must, ultimately, be responsible for resolving the future of Asia.

In each Asian country the universities will be the pinnacles of the educational system of the country as a whole. They will be fed from the schools, and they will not only contribute to the total school system but also make their presence felt throughout the societies in which they exist. A principal task of education must be to break down prejudices and established ideas which have little or no relevance to life on the eve of the twenty-first century. There is much in Asian culture which is of universal and eternal value, but at the same time there are certain elements in it which militate against advances towards rationality. For example, there are still many peoples in Asia who do not eat eggs as part of their daily diet, only because of the symbolic value of the egg in their culture. Many Chinese in Malaya still refrain from eating bean sprouts, which are cheap, plentiful, and very nutritious, and this only because their low price is such as to associate them with poverty.

By 1984, as a result of the spread and influence of education, most of these little barriers will have been eroded, and it is even possible that the Asian countries will find themselves in a state of preparedness to take up the challenges which stand at the threshold of the next century.

PATTERNS OF PROGRESS

by Professor Kaname Hayashi

Chairman, Section on Economics, Commerce, and Business Administration, Science Council of Japan

In visualizing Asia in 1984 I must make a number of assumptions: first and foremost, that large-scale warfare will no longer be considered possible; secondly, that the cooperation between the U.S.A. and the U.S.S.R. will be limited, while the present conflict of views between Red China and the U.S.S.R. will be resolved; and thirdly that capitalist countries will continue to seek to exercise a kind of economic imperialism in Asia.

On these assumptions, I believe that Asia will develop, in two decades, a social map roughly as follows:

(1) The countries with planned economies will make remarkable advances. In Siberia, China, Mongolia, etc. the automation of production processes, the growth in output of consumer goods, and the development of transport will greatly reduce those differences in standards between city and countryside

which characterize life in Asia today, and will promote the prosperity of both.

(2) The geographical nonsenses that exist today in the separation of North and South Korea and North and South Vietnam will have been brought to an end, but it is conceivable that the intervention of the United States will postpone, even for two decades, the re-unification of Red China and Taiwan.

(3) In spite of outside military and economic support for *coups d'état*, and also in spite of the extreme poverty of the people, the efforts of the countries in South-east Asia to escape from their difficulties will be marked by a stronger sense of national independence and neutralism and by forms of economic development suited to their needs rather than to foreign preconceptions. Here, one thinks of Laos, Cambodia, Burma, and Indonesia. In particular the efforts of Indonesia to establish a socialist economy may have a great influence on the whole of southern Asia in the coming twenty years. Although the economies of both Malaysia and the Philippines are at an extremely low level of development, moves towards planned economies may be opposed by Britain and by the U.S.A., respectively, depending on political developments in those 'mother countries' themselves. We must expect, in any case, that Malaysia and the Philippines, together with Thailand, will find it difficult to escape from the influences of the former colonial powers. The same can be said of the countries in south-western Asia.

(4) I am pessimistic about India, the second largest country in Asia. In addition to the social backwardness prevailing over her vast territory, and the chaos which comes from the complexity of race, religion, the caste system, and language differences, the extreme poverty of most of her people will prevent India from developing modern industries as fast as she would wish in the coming twenty years.

(5) Lastly, Japan is a special case, and her development will be an almost theatrical feature of the two decades up to 1984. Whether the plot may turn out to be a tragedy or comedy, Japan, in the meanwhile, will strive towards a happy ending and will somehow make a step forward into a planned economy. Japan is the capitalist leading lady amid the feudalism and socialism of Asia, but her costume is medieval and her heart remains even

servile. While proudly putting herself with the advanced countries in the West by joining the O.E.C.D., Japan is mal-
developed, wanting the capacity even to ratify the International
Labour Organisation's Treaty No. 87 which lays down basic
conditions for workers. American affluence co-exists with cheap
labour in Japan; a feudal authoritarian spirit, powerful labour
organizations, and a progressive intelligentsia are intermixed. In
short, many basic contradictions are ripe for resolution. We may
expect that a quite different course will be followed from that of
the capitalist countries of the West. Twenty years seems long
enough for Japan to prepare, democratically, for the establishment of a planned economy.

There is a saying, 'Light comes from the Orient'. It appears
to some of us in Asia that European culture has come to a dead
end, and that the light of a new culture will come from the East.
What manner of 'light'?

We must remember that, even at the zenith of Greece and
Rome, far older civilizations existed in the East. When the tide
of the industrial revolution swept through Europe and North
America, it produced the contemporary culture, promoted
capitalism, and made possible the colonialization of all the
countries of Asia excepting Japan. Today, the development of
the whole economy of Asia is remarkably behind that of the
West, and the people's life is one of extreme poverty. The underdevelopment of Asia cannot be remedied merely by the introduction of technology and monetary aid. The situation cannot
be improved, but only worsened, by external threats or by *coups
d'état*. Now economic and social ideas are necessary, and the new
political structures in which they can materialize.

The 'light' from the East, then, will take the form of a social
inventiveness whereby, in the face of almost overwhelming problems of initial poverty, hunger, and rising populations, the benefits of modern technical inventions can be made available to the
underprivileged of the world. Asia seems ready to proceed
gradually in this direction in the next twenty years. A Japanese
proverb says, 'A slow crow may gain in the end'. Asia, which is
now so far behind the development of the capitalist industrial
economies, may, thanks to its very backwardness, be in a fortunate state from which it can leapfrog to a new way of life. I

should like to be able to verify these hopes for 'the light that comes from the Orient' by reference to the actual economic map of Asia in 1984.

PROSPECTS FOR CHINA
by Joan Robinson

Let us first assume that the present trend of development in China rolls smoothly on for the next twenty years, and then inquire in what conditions we could expect it to do so.

The restoration of law and order in 1949 and the rapid spread of elementary hygiene created an enormous population bulge. The authorities are now alive to the necessity of getting the birth-rate down to match the reduced death-rate. They advocate late marriage and family planning. The emancipation of women, which seems to be more complete and more completely accepted by men in China than anywhere else, will no doubt help. But even if numbers are in sight of stabilizing for the future in 1984, there cannot but have been a great increase meanwhile. Demographic statistics are not available, but it is loosely said that half of the present population is under eighteen years of age.

In spite of an increase in the adult population of perhaps 200 millions, food supplies will be sufficient to provide a better standard of diet than the present one, which is more or less adequate. This will have been brought about partly by opening up and settling now vacant land, principally in the north-west, but mainly by increasing productivity in the old settled areas by improved techniques, a massive use of artificial fertilizers, and by the extension of multiple cropping through improved irrigation. The population of pigs and poultry will have risen more than in proportion to the population of humans. The habit of using dairy products, and the dairy farms to provide them, will have grown; fish farms will be common, and supplies of fruit and vegetables superabundant.

The standard of life in respect of simple necessities, clothing and household goods, consumer durables, and domestic use of electricity will have risen out of recognition – industrial output will have at least doubled and redoubled, and light industry supplying consumer goods will have had its full share.

All the same the proportion of the population in the agricultural sector (at present five sixths) will not have fallen dramatically. The growth of the industrial labour force and the city population will not have done more, at best, than absorb the increase in the adult population. Mechanization of agriculture and transport, which releases labour without increasing output, will have been kept in check. The fantastic polarity of Chinese industry, where sweating men are pulling cartloads of materials to the doors of a fully automatic plant, will not have been very much reduced.

Control of the growth of cities will have continued. With every new plant set up, housing for the workers is provided and a drift into town in search of jobs that do not exist will have been prevented. At the same time, there will have been a drive to break down the sharp differences between town and country life so as to check the drift from the other end. The blaze of industrial production within the agricultural communes went off at half-cock during the 'Great Leap' in 1958, but the basic idea was not forgotten and will have been gradually and soberly developed, so that tool shops and tractor parks on the farms will satisfy the urge of young men to handle machinery. Motor scooters (horrid thought!) will be seen where now a bicycle is an envied treasure. Handicrafts will have developed into small cooperative factories. The schools in the communes will have developed into rural colleges. There will be cinemas and theatres for local opera in the villages.

The great cities will have become much like cities anywhere else except that they will have been developed with an eye to preserving amenities. The old slums (which have already been cleaned up) will have been rebuilt. The latest buildings will be agreeable, for by then the architects will have found how to translate the Chinese sense of line and proportion into modern requirements and modern materials, but many lumpish buildings put up under Russian influence will still be in use.

The Roman alphabet will have made headway, though the ideographs will not yet have been displaced. Cultural life will be rich and varied, all the old arts of China flourishing side by side

with western drama, music, and ballet; but western vulgarity
will not have been allowed to leak in.

What are the necessary conditions for all this to be realized?
First and foremost, of course, that China is allowed to develop in
peace. We should hope, for our own sakes, that the shameful
farce of Taiwan in the United Nations will have long since been
wound up and that China will be playing a full part in international life. For her, however, this is not so important. Given
peace, isolation has certain advantages.

On the other hand, the growth of trade with the West, including Japan, would help appreciably to speed up industrial development. From the point of view of trade, the breach with the
Soviets will turn out to be, as the Chinese say, 'a bad thing
turned into a good thing'. Russia supplied to China equipment
designed for her own needs – a plant, for instance, to produce
the heavy tractors used on the Steppes – while capitalist firms, in
the tradition that the customer is always right, will tailor supplies
to Chinese requirements. Exchange of know-how and training of
technicians and scientists would be very helpful but not indis-
pensable.

The second condition is that the Chinese government does not
feel obliged to enter the nuclear arms race, which would wreck
the economy and undermine political stability by keeping the
people's belts too tight for too long.

A third condition is that the Chinese Communist Party should
keep its virtue. The Chinese revolution is still in the heroic
phase, in which it inspires the kind of redeeming devotion which
one imagines in the first generation of a great new religion. The
administration is uncorrupted. The standard of honesty, public
and private, may be as high in Sweden – it certainly is not here.
The Party is continuously 'rectifying' itself: anyone who takes
advantage of his position as a Party member for selfish ends or
who indulges in 'bossism' to his subordinates is quickly exposed.
Everyone lives simply. The absence of conspicuous consumption is a great economic asset. Can human nature bear the strain
of such high standards for another twenty years and more?

Chinese people themselves are very worried about the problem
of the 'lucky children' – the generation who have had everything
handed to them ready made. They speak very bitterly of the

nepotism and graft which they believe have developed in Russia, and they study how to bring up their young people so that it will not happen to them. The time of frugality, hard work, and a slow rise in comfort from the bottom upwards will not be over in twenty years (it could be over in a decade if the population had not been rising) and if luxury and wangling crept in at the top, sulkiness at the bottom would soon let the economy drift into stagnation. Economic development is a moral problem.

The World in 1984

OPTIMISTS VERSUS PESSIMISTS

by Dr Anne McLaren

Looking twenty years ahead, two problems dwarf all others: the possibility of nuclear war, and the extent of hunger among the world's augmented billions. On both, *New Scientist*'s star-studded team of world experts show remarkable unanimity.

Three or four out of nearly 100 contributions explicitly assumed that no major war would take place during the next twenty years. The others ignored the possibility completely. Asked to forecast conditions in 1984 'on the basis of known possibilities and trends', no one forecast nuclear devastation. Perhaps we may draw comfort from this.

All who touched on the world food problem drew the same moral: 'We could feed them if we tried.' 'The world has enough resources – technical, scientific, and material – to eliminate poverty, disease, and an early death, for the whole human race' (Professor Salam, Vol. 1, page 16). 'There is little doubt that technically on a world-wide scale these increases' – i.e. the required increases in total food supplies and in animal foods – 'can be achieved' (Dr Sen, Vol. 1, page 59). 'The technical problems' – i.e. of agriculture in the less-developed countries – 'are not hard to solve' (Sir William Slater, Vol. 1, page 63). 'The major problems facing the continent' (Africa) 'can be solved if knowledge already available is widely applied' (Dr Sai, page 167).

Some unconventional sources of food were discussed. 'Can we not save the starving children of the world with krill? I am sure we shall' (Sir Alister Hardy, Vol. 1, page 100). Dr Sai suggests weaning African toddlers on to bacterially dewaxed petroleum products. Professor Waddington (page 13) points out that recent advances in achieving protein synthesis *in vitro* offer the theoretical possibility of synthesis of proteins by ribosomes on a factory scale. But the main emphasis throughout is on the adequacy, even in 1984, of conventional methods of agriculture, *if they were adequately applied*.

At this point we come up against a segregation into optimists and pessimists: 'Twenty years from now . . . the less-developed world will be as hungry, as relatively undeveloped, and as desperately poor, as today' (Professor Salam, loc. cit.). 'While the gap' (between the income and standards of living of rich and poor countries) 'will continue to exist, it should be considerably reduced' (Mr White, page 112). 'The affluent states will be becoming more affluent, and the underdeveloped states will be hard-pressed even to maintain existing living standards as their populations increase' (Dr Burton, page 117). 'The income gap between the rich and the poor countries will probably be wider than now in absolute terms. In relative terms it may not be radically different from what it is today' (Professor Kristensen, pages 108–9). 'By 1984 the scientists will have achieved their major goal, the drafting and general acceptance of a new system of education, based on the ideals of fundamental common interests of the human species, and on the development of a sense of belonging to mankind as a whole' (Professor Rotblat, page 121). 'The increase in wealth and leisure should, by 1984, have forced us to abandon, as a major source of human effort, the one-against-all competitiveness which we have relied on so much hitherto' (Professor Waddington, loc. cit.). (cf. 'Private enterprise will be esteemed as never before', Professor Baker, page 140.)

Even from the economists and political scientists who have contributed to this series, little hard thinking has emerged on the basic question of how the world is likely to develop economically. The general assumption seems to be that if the underdeveloped countries were to be developed and the starving millions fed, it would be because feelings of decency and humanity and rationality finally prevailed in the richer countries. The pessimists hold that this is unlikely to happen by 1984 ('unless, of course, there rises earlier somewhere a new Messiah, the one who can preach that in this age when technological miracles are indeed possible the raising of living standards everywhere to a decent human level is first and foremost a moral problem, and a collective world responsibility', Professor Salam, loc. cit.); the optimists (Professor Rotblat, for example) usually cast scientists in the role of Salam's Messiah, foreseeing that scientists and computers will increasingly take over the responsibilities of government, until (in 1984 ?) the world will at last be run in a relatively rational manner.

Yet it was not feelings of decency and humanity and rationality on the part of the rich which led to the more equitable distribution of incomes within, for instance, Great Britain. Victorian charitable organizations did much to alleviate individual suffering, but little to raise the standard of living of the working classes.

The I.G.Y. and the Years of the Quiet Sun may be succeeded by an H.W.Y. (Hungry World Year); but if one is realistic, does it not seem more likely, on economic grounds, that a larger impetus will come from the trend, already noticeable, for industrial concerns in developed countries to set up subsidiaries, taking advantage of the cheap labour force available in those countries of Africa, Asia, and South America which still remain outside the Communist bloc ? Workers have to be fed, otherwise they cannot work; workers in modern factories also have to be educated.

A welfare world can hardly be expected by 1984; but if it ever comes to pass, it will surely be through pressure of economic forces, rather than by a scientists' take-over bid for world government, or by Messianic intervention.

The segregation into optimists and pessimists is apparent throughout the series, on every theme. Scientists tend to be more optimistic than non-scientists, Americans more optimistic than Europeans.

Here is an American scientist, extreme perhaps in his starry-eyedness but not untypical: 'The ability to create environmental conditions which can maintain ideal climate, pure air, and freedom from noise will make available to the average [sic] home dweller the seclusion and comfort once limited to those who could afford the luxury of travel to nature's resort spots. ... With the possibilities of greater leisure ... interest should turn to cultural development and creative hobbies. ... Through a better understanding of his fellow man ... mankind can be released from fears based on ignorance, and the suspicions and hatred those fears bring about' (Mr Carter, pages 37–9). Contrast a British non-scientist: 'The arts, in any historical meaning of the word, will have disappeared. . . . There will be lights everywhere except in the mind of man, and the fall of the last civilization will not be heard above the incessant din' (Sir Herbert Read, pages 91–2).

Read also achieves the most pessimistically improbable single prediction: 'Composers like Beethoven, Wagner, and Stravinsky will be forgotten.' For optimistic improbability, I like: 'by 1984 . . . we should understand what the brain does when we think' (Lord Brain, page 9). And the weather? Here the pessimists predominate. 'In the temperate latitudes, there will always be a residual uncertainty in a forecast of weather for a day or two ahead. . . . In 1984 British weather will be much as it always has been' (Sir Graham Sutton, Vol. 1, page 105). *Plus ça change . . .*

THE WORLD OF THE SCIENTIST

by Professor Frank Press
Director of Seismographical Laboratory, California Institute of Technology

This series of articles on 1984 is remarkable not only for its authoritative preview of science of the future, but also for the brief glimpse it allows us of the style and personality of the many eminent contributors. Nowhere does a scientist reveal so much of himself as when he gives his imagination free flight. Most of the pieces begin with a disclaimer in which the dangers of prediction are recognized, and the extrapolation to the future proceeds from known initial conditions and trends. And yet, in not a few places one finds a phantasmagoric depiction of things to come befitting the best of Wells, Orwell, or Huxley.

As a scientist who hopes to be professionally active in 1984, albeit in the twilight of his career, I would have enjoyed reading more about the style and pace of science two decades hence. Will the presently accelerating trend towards finer and finer subdivision of disciplines with the concomitant production of narrow specialists continue? As a result, will we witness a plethora of insignificant discoveries, or will team research provide the collective skill, knowledge, experience from which great science will emerge? Is it evident that the rate of increase of support of science must diminish (at least in the U.S.A.)? Will this mean a decreasing emphasis on the massive approach so well represented by projects Mohole and Apollo, by $100-million accelerators? What will become of the individual scientist and his small project? Will this be a time when disciplines (let alone sub-fields) will be actively competing against each other for the science dollar? If so, who will establish priorities and what will the criteria be?

What about the scientist in public affairs? Will we see the emergence of a new breed of scientist-statesman? Will he be qualified in science as a creator or an appreciator? Or will public disenchantment with scientists in government result in the return of the part-time, commuting consultant?

With regard to questions such as these, the extrapolation over two decades is less certain because the initial conditions are not fixed, and the trends have yet to be recognized. Twenty years from now, I probably will wish that I had stopped with this disclaimer.

I would guess that in 1984 science and technology will enjoy an even greater prosperity than now. Justification in terms of 'national prestige' will still be fashionable. More important will be the need to maintain government spending (in the least controversial way) in the face of reduced military budgets. The big project will still be with us – as a boost to the economy and as a means of showing the flag. Many scientists will question the basis for this often wasteful support, but most will find themselves enjoying the prosperity.

The individual investigator and his small project will not become antiquated. Many first-class people will still choose this manner of conducting their research – as a matter of taste, if not to maintain their individuality. We will need them, and we will be able to afford them. Team research will be the big thing, with specialists crossing fields; the physicists working in biology, the information theory specialist contributing to geophysics will be commonplace. Abandoned fields will be revitalized by contributions from workers in other disciplines who need new results to further their own research. Thus, advances in classical physics will be made by engineers and geophysicists. Expect as many papers in applied mathematics from institutes of biology and oceanography as from mathematics centres. Social sciences, aided and abetted by the sciences, will become respectable in the sense of qualifying for large-scale support.

The big projects involving thousands of scientists and hundreds of thousands of workers will be in evidence. Lunar exploration with roving vehicles and fixed observatories will be recent history, and we will be concerned with observatories on Mars. High-energy physicists will be working with machines in the billion-dollar range. Biologists may be obtaining much support from space agencies, and the oceanographic fleet will exceed the size of some navies.

Scientists will be involved in high-level government decisions as advisers on about the same basis as now. We will not see scientists in politics; it will still be a distasteful field for the intellectual. We will see them intimately involved in selecting research priorities. However, despite the rumblings we now hear, I would guess that competition for support will not yet be so keen as to be a major issue. I see prosperous times, a quicker pace, a flashier style. Much wasteful effort will occur, more so than now, but hopefully never as much as with military research and development. Great discoveries will be made; they will be shockingly expensive by present standards, but the money to pay for them will be there.

INCINERATION, INHUMANITY, OR IMMORTALITY?

by Desmond King-Hele

The contributors to this series are asked to forecast conditions in 1984 on the basis of known trends. The pace of progress in the next twenty years may well be about twice as rapid as in the past forty years, so the most logical way of extrapolating is presumably to note the differences between 1924 and 1964, and then to apply the same 'factor of advance' between 1964 and 1984. This pedantic procedure is rather discouraging. Between 1924 and 1964 the explosive power of weapons increased by a factor of over a million, and extrapolation of known trends therefore implies another increase by a factor of a million before 1984. Even now, civilization would have little chance of surviving a major conflict; by 1984 that chance will be much smaller.

It is also rather depressing that we have received no certain communication from the forms of life far superior to ours which ought to have evolved in other favourable environments in the universe. Have superior forms failed to develop, then, because the evolutionary process carries with it a built-in death sentence? Is the power of the world to destroy itself always attained before it has learnt how to modify the inherited aggressive impulses instilled by aeons of evolutionary struggle? Every 'right-thinking person' instinctively rejects such an idea, because our own evolution has endowed us with an innate optimism, which revives hope even in the face of hopeless difficulties. The cynic may write off this 'unquenchable spirit of man' as a refusal to face unpleasant facts, reflected on a wider scale when a government has to say there is no cause for alarm even when there is. Whatever the diagnosis, the optimism exists, and I share it.

So, like the other contributors, I shall ignore the darker possibilities and make the happy assumptions that man will still be dominating the earth in 1984 and that science will advance smoothly. If so, how will human beings be living in 1984? Today the situation is paradoxical: on the one hand, the underdeveloped nations have a large proportion of their peoples underfed, and the proportion may be increasing because of high birth-rates; on the other hand, the 'advanced' nations spend vast sums on 'defence' against each other, an activity which is the more paradoxical since none has achieved an effective defence, in the normal sense of the word. Will man's inhumanity to man continue, or will indifference to the plight of the wretched seem as intolerable to advanced man in 1984 as the slave trade seems now? 'So long as the name of country and the selfish conceptions which it includes shall subsist', the inhumanity is likely to continue: 'world patriotism' is slowly growing, it is true, and if we are to survive much beyond 1984 world government will be essential, as Professor Rotblat emphasizes. But world government is unlikely to have come by 1984, and, as Professor Salam remarks, the less-developed nations will be no better off in 1984 unless there is a powerful and protracted crusade – which as yet shows little sign of even beginning. So the advanced peoples (and the ruling classes in many underdeveloped countries) will probably be slow to learn compassion towards the starving peoples of the under-developed lands.

Perhaps the most effective way of fostering the growth of such compassion would be through the development of a world religion. This is most unlikely, however, since belief in super-natural powers will presumably continue to decline: as Lady Wootton remarked, a secular morality is required. The decline of religious belief will have advantages, for many vexed social questions may be settled more rationally and be less bedevilled by ingrained dogmas which seem absurd except to one sect. At present religion is valuable as psychotherapy, and helps all those who need a prop of faith to save them from despair or more serious mental illness and who like to have an insurance against death. But these motives for religion would decline if it were possible to alleviate the dire poverty which promotes despair and makes death familiar, and if mental illnesses could gradually be traced to their physiological roots, as foreseen in the articles by Lord Brain and Sir Aubrey Lewis.

In technology, especially those branches already well supported financially, prediction seems to be relatively easy and the various articles show an impressive unanimity. The most important advances will probably come rather in medicine and biology, since the comparatively small amount of money now devoted to these subjects will probably be increased, and because discoveries can quickly be put to practical use. Here current trends are a poor guide, and one can only guess what the key discoveries will be.

My guess is that the most important will be the elucidation of ageing. Since its onset is so imperceptible, ageing may well be only a minor biochemical change, which, once clarified, may be controllable: 'research may show that ... degeneration is not inevitable in the aged human being', as Sir Charles Dodds cautiously remarks in his article; or, 'the period of youth and vigour may be indefinitely extended', as Erasmus Darwin ex-uberantly forecast over 150 years ago. The last ten years have unexpectedly fulfilled one of man's age-old dreams, space travel; if research into ageing is stepped up, the next ten years may point the way to the end of that other quest, for the elixir of life. If so, the social, administrative, and ethical problems will be appalling. We should consider soon how to act if immortality is imminent, instead of leaving the problems entirely to the writers of science fiction.

A PROSPEROUS BUT UNBEAUTIFUL WORLD?

by Professor S. Chandrasekhar

Department of Physics, University of Mysore

Science will of course be the major force in the development of society in the next twenty years. Investment in science and technology will be greater than ever before, and consequently we may expect to see a considerable improvement in living standards throughout the world. The changes will be spectacular in those countries which are already advanced technologically, and will lead to much better living conditions and more leisure. In the poorer countries the rate of progress will no doubt be slower, but when reckoned in terms of basic human needs the changes will be no less significant. Furthermore, there is an increasing awareness in all countries that the plight of the less fortunate human beings is to some extent a collective responsibility, and this is indeed a good sign. Altogether, I think life will certainly be better in material respects in the coming years.

With the growing scientific knowledge of the human mind, is there any risk of governments obtaining new means of controlling mass behaviour autocratically? This is a difficult question to answer, but there are some clear trends which indicate that it is unlikely to happen in the near future. For one thing, we are certainly progressing towards universal education. It is true that educational standards vary a great deal and, generally speaking, need improvement – indeed there will soon have to be a revolution in teaching methods to cope with the explosion in knowledge – but it is fair to say that the conditioning process in schools is essentially quite sound. As far as I know, nowhere is the education directed deliberately towards authoritarianism, militarism, or total subservience. Secondly, we may reasonably expect that there will be more leisure in the coming years. It may give rise to a host of new problems, but at the same time leisure does breed a certain amount of healthy scepticism which is necessary for the stability of a good society. So, in my opinion, there is no reason to be pessimistic about the future of the human race.

However, in our anxiety to improve our lot we are ruthlessly exterminating the wild life on this planet. The process of destruction, which has been going on for a long time, has accelerated to an alarming degree in the last few decades. Indiscriminate hunting and organized poaching are taking their disastrous toll every year, and there remains only a pitifully small fraction of the game that existed fifty years ago. The rapid deforestation and devegetation brought about by the rise in human population are pushing the animals from their natural habitats, so that even the few that remain have little chance of survival.

Yet it is surprising how few of us are fully aware of the urgency of the problem. Animals are being massacred by the hundreds and thousands, not merely for the meat, but also for their tails which make good fly whisks, or for their horns which possess magical powers of rejuvenation, or for their tusks which look so well in the smoking room. In India the lion, the snow leopard, the cheetah, the one-horned rhino, the two-horned rhino, the Kashmir stag, and the deer are fast declining in number and facing extinction. (In fact, it is feared that the cheetah and the two-horned rhino are already extinct.) It is an even more tragic story in Africa. Areas which a few years ago were literally teeming with game of incredible variety are now sadly depleted – and still the killing goes on. In the concluding chapter of his book *Operation Noah*, Charles Lagus asks: 'Is this whole venture just quixotic and stupid ? . . . isn't the game of Africa doomed to die out anyway ?' That about sums up the outlook for the future. By 1984 the rape will probably be complete, and the vast continents of Asia and Africa will be empty and unbeautiful.

There is just the hope that, if the national and international wild-life organizations join forces and make an all-out effort, they may succeed in preserving what we have. But, for such a programme to be really effective, we have first to convince ourselves and our fellow men that saving those animals is nearly as important for the human condition as saving mankind.

Summing Up
by Nigel Calder

What follows is my attempt to summarize as concisely as possible the main predictions and problems for the next twenty years that arise from the contributions to the 1984 series. In interpreting the picture that emerges, we should bear in mind the limitations in the method of collecting the contributions. Expert contributors were asked to forecast conditions in 1984 on the basis of known possibilities and trends, rather than to speculate freely. The series was planned by *New Scientist*, with some preconceptions of what subjects were important and what the experts might say about them. Accordingly, the discussion has not been entirely 'open-ended'. There are some obvious gaps, both in topics and in national representation. Some topics (for example, *weapons*, *business*, *law*, and *religion*) were deliberately excluded. Others were not obtained in time for inclusion: these were *Europe* and *U.S.S.R.* as main topics, and *earth sciences*, *pipelines*, and *buildings* as subsidiary topics.

Great efforts were made to make the series as international as possible, but in the outcome there has been great reliance on British, American, and French contributions. Some of the thirteen Russians approached at first agreed to take part but, late in the day, they all withdrew at once. It seemed like a political ruling.

It is not possible here to convey the nuances such as 'almost certainly' or 'can reasonably expect' with which many of the authors qualify their statements. Where there is explicit disagreement or implicit controversy on important points, I have posed them as questions.

TABLE A MAJOR TECHNICAL REVOLUTIONS

Character of change	Technical aspects	Possibilities arising	Effects on the individual	Social aspects	Global aspects
I. Revolution in information: vast increases in computing and telecommunications capacity, and wide use of electronic storage and retrieval of information.	Computers a good deal faster and easier to 'converse' with. Computers linked in nation-wide and world-wide networks. Messages by computer network (in digital code). Big increase in communications using millimetre radio, laser beams or communications satellites.	Television-telephones. 'Dialling' for news, books, etc. World-wide weather and disaster warning services using satellites.	Ready access to information (a data store in the home?). Close surveillance by government computers? Use of television links instead of business travel.	'Abolition' of libraries, paperwork and typists. Wide use of computers in every field of activity. Increase in local broadcasting. No more newspapers as we know them?	World-wide instantaneous reporting. Language translation. Big investment in communications (but increasing nationalism in these services?).
2. Revolutionary consequences of biology.	Understanding of living systems, including the human brains. Manipulation of genetic structure. Development of 'bio-engineering'. Understanding of ageing process.	'Biochemical machines' for food production, energy transformation, chemical manufacture, and information storage. Alteration of cell heredity. New Engineering controls modelled on biological systems.	Longer life. Better treatment of mental disease. Inhibition of ageing or 'medicated survival'? Loss of individuality by surgical implantation?	Better understanding of human behaviour. Need for moral criteria in biological manipulations. Danger of a racket in transplantable organs. Danger of 'mind control'.	Understanding of complexity of living systems. Opportunities for enlarging food production.

3. The beginning of the exploitation of the oceans.	Fish-rearing and transplanting. Fish concentrators. Mid-water trawls. Working on the sea-bed at 600 fathoms. Obtaining minerals from sea-water and the sea-bed.	Transplantation of organs and wide use of artificial limbs and organs. Modification of the developing brain. Conquest of viruses, heart disease, and cancer? Use of 'new' protein sources (squid, red fish, Antarctic krill). Control of weather and climate by warming or cooling sea-water?	New way of life for some. Better coastal resorts and sea ports.		UN ownership of ocean floor? UN surveillance of climate - control experiments?
4. New forms of energy.	Big increase in generating efficiency (including 'MHD' methods). Wide use of fuel cells as small power units and for energy storage. Growth in nuclear (fission) power. Demonstration of power generation by controlled fusion.	'Footloose' industries. Large-scale desalting of water.	Fuel-cell generators in the home. Fuel-cell batteries for cars.	Decentralization of power generation? Quieter road transport.	Shift of populations to regions where water and conventional energy sources are scarce.

TABLE B EVOLUTIONARY CHANGES

Pattern of change	Some factors	Some consequences
1. A continuing race between food and population.	50–60 per cent increase in world population. Conquest of some major diseases leading to 50 per cent increase in expectation of life of children in poorer countries. Food production unlikely to keep pace in poorer countries of Asia. Less land will be required for producing foods that can be synthesized. Farming becoming a 'science-based' industry in the richer countries.	Agrarian reform required in many of the poorer countries. Increase in food exports from richer to poorer nations. People will have to eat unaccustomed foods. Huge investment in water supplies required.
2. General industrial progress, including automation.	Extensive use of numerical control in high-speed automatic workshops. Greater use of automatic aids in aircraft, ships, trains, and cars. Use of 'designed' materials in engineering, including very strong steels and bio-logical-like composite materials. Energy use more than doubled. Three- to four-fold increase in air travel (?) and a big jump in air freight. Five-fold increase in petrochemical production.	Prosperity linked with investment in auto-mation. More 'scientific' management and closer links between science and industry. Opportunities for decentralization with small-scale automated plant. Fewer workers on the land and in factories; more in service, marketing, and research activities. Growth in the middle class. Glorification of 'work' cannot endure.
3. Growth in knowledge.	Mathematical theories of complex systems. More plausible theories of the universe and the fundamental particles. Possible surprises from landings on the moon and from biological exploration of Mars. Understanding of the dynamical processes of the earth's and the sun's weather. Knowledge of the Earth's upper mantle. Emergence of the social sciences. Growth in biological knowledge as in Table A (2).	

4. Life even more oriented towards the family and the home.	New materials and labour-saving devices. Domestic robots. 'Ideal climate' in the home. Almost limitless access to information from the living room. Growth in automatic merchandizing.	Higher status of women.
5. A great advancement of education.	Recognition of the economic importance of education. Wide use of teaching machines, programmed instruction, radio, and television. Development of better methods of teaching. Growth in adult education and re-training. Emphasis on science and technology in the poorer countries.	Wider literacy (90 per cent of the world's children at school compared with 50 per cent today). Teaching better suited to the individual student. Broader-minded education and more humanistic teaching of science. Re-assessment of the role of the teacher.

TABLE C CONFLICTS AND CHOICES

Points at issue	Relevant scientific factors	Social and political factors
1. World development: is it going to happen fast enough to make the poor richer?	Technical knowledge could have spectacular effects (e.g. in health and agriculture) if the resources were available to apply it.	Will the gap between rich and poor countries widen or narrow? 'Furious crusade' against poverty needed? Better conditions of trade for poorer nations? Trading groups among poorer countries (federation?). Social revolution needed, e.g. in Latin America?
2. International relations: war, cold war, coexistence or co-operation?	Thermonuclear war would be disastrous. Spread of 'independent nuclear deterrents'? Bigger international scientific effort — in laboratories, weather centres, space exploration, etc. Development of 'peace research'.	Numerous small conflicts. Racial conflict. Rich versus poor nations conflicts? Increasing nationalism and isolationism? Increasing trade. International commercial enterprises. 'Middle path' for less developed countries? Scientists as peacemakers?
3. Government: will it be more or less democratic, more or less rational?	State power increased by big computers. Danger of 'mind control'. Computer simulation and operational research in policy-making. Possibility of 'instant' polls of the whole population on current issues. Increased scientific advice for government.	More far-sighted and 'logistic' outlook in government. Increased knowledge of facts narrowing the range of choice. More 'professional' politicians; more critical electors. New political theories?
4. Ecological attitudes: what will become of the natural environment?	Continuing pollution? Wild life doomed except in reserves? Better knowledge of soils and biological interactions.	Wiser planning of land-use and landscapes? More use of land for recreation.

5. Cities: squeeze or sprawl?

Urban studies advancing.
Better means of transport or restrictions on traffic?
Very cheap buildings leading to impermanence?

Vast growth in cities (Calcutta 30 million?).
Turmoil in and around many cities.
Cities centred on universities? Or airports?

6. The individual in 1984: will he enjoy life?

Increase in neuroses.
More use of behaviour-influencing drugs.
Malnutrition from eating the wrong foods?
Invention of new gambling games.

Not *much* shorter working week, but longer holidays.
More crime?
More generous provision for the old and the sick.
Disenchantment about economic growth?
Need for a secular morality?
Need for 'the humanities' to question ends and means.

Notes on the Contributors

NIGEL CALDER has been editor of *New Scientist* since 1962. Educated at Cambridge, he worked two years as physicist for Mullard Research Laboratories before joining the staff of *New Scientist* at its inception in 1956.

WALTER RUSSELL BRAIN (Knowing our minds better) was President of the British Association for the Advancement of Science 1963–4 and Consulting Physician to the London Hospital and the Maida Vale Hospital for Nervous Diseases. Author of *Recent Advances in Neurology* and *Diseases of the Nervous System,* he was recently elected a Fellow of the Royal Society for 'outstanding services to the advancement of medicine'.

CONRAD HAL WADDINGTON (Science and wisdom) is Buchanan Professor of Genetics in the University of Edinburgh and President of the International Union of Biological Sciences. Elected Fellow of the Royal Society in 1947, his most recent works are *New Patterns in Genetics and Development* and *The Nature of Life.*

HERBERT RICHARD HOGGART (The humanities and wisdom) is Professor of English at Birmingham University. Best known as the author of *The Uses of Literacy.* He served on the Albemarle and Pilkington Committees.

JOHN ALEXANDER CHARLES (Stretching the expectation of life) is Consultant Director of the World Health Organization, Geneva. Previously, he was Chief Medical Officer to the Ministry of Health, the Ministry of Education, and the Home Office, from 1950 to 1960. He was President of the twelfth World Health Assembly. He was knighted in 1950, and has received several awards for his work.

EDWARD CHARLES DODDS (The three great problems) is President of the Royal College of Physicians, Courtauld Professor of Biochemistry in the University of London, and Director of the Courtauld Institute of Biochemistry at the Middlesex Hospital. He is past chairman of the Committee of Management of the Cancer Research Institute. He was knighted in 1954, and created a baronet in 1964.

ZENON BACQ (A vicious circle of chemicals against chemicals?) is sixty. He is Professor of Physiopathology and Radiobiology in the

University of Liège, Belgium. Besides teaching he is also engaged in research, and lectures abroad. He has been awarded several prizes for his scientific work, and is the author of a number of books.

AUBREY LEWIS (Changes in psychiatric methods and attitudes) was educated in Australia. He has been Professor of Psychiatry in the University of London since 1946. He is also Civilian Consultant in Psychiatry to the R.A.F. He was knighted in 1959.

EMMETT FINLEY CARTER (Homes of the future) is sixty-two. He was director of the Institute of Radio Engineers from 1943-5, and is now a member of the board of directors of the Stanford Research Institute, California, of which he was once President. He was awarded the Outstanding Civilian Service Award given by the Secretary of the Army in 1963.

MEREDITH WOOLDRIDGE THRING (A robot about the house) joined the British Iron and Steel Research Association in 1946 and later became assistant director. In 1962 he was made President of the Institute of Fuel. He has been Professor of Fuel Technology and Chemical Engineering at the University of Sheffield since 1953.

MICHAEL YOUNG (Changing patterns of family life) was educated at the University of London, was called to the bar, and later became director of Political and Economic Planning. He is now the director of the Institute of Community Studies, Bethnal Green, London, chairman of the Consumers' Association, the Advisory Centre for Education, the Research Institute of Consumer Affairs, and the National Extension College. He lectures in sociology at Cambridge.

ASA BRIGGS (Unconditional surrender to facts?) is forty-two. He has been Professor of History in the University of Leeds, and is now Pro-Vice Chancellor and Dean of the School of Social Studies in the University of Sussex. He is President of the Workers' Educational Association.

VLADIMIR ZWORYKIN (Communications and government) was a Vice-President of the Radio Corporation of America Laboratories from 1947 to 1954, when he was appointed Honorary Vice-President of the R.C.A. He is also Director of the Medical Electronics Center at the Rockefeller Institute, New York.

RICHARD STONE (Computer models of the economy) is P. D. Leake Professor of Finance and Accounting in the University of Cambridge, where he was previously Director of the Department of Applied Economics. At present he is directing a research group which is building a computable model of the British economy.

ALEXANDER KING ('Report of the Council for Science Policy, 1983–4') has been Senior Lecturer in chemistry at Imperial College, London. He is now Director for Scientific Affairs of the Organization for European Cooperation and Development, and has held several other important posts with the OEEC.

RENÉ MAHEU (Universal literacy in the age of technology) is fifty-nine. He was educated at the École Normale Supérieure and at the Sorbonne. He has been Director-General of UNESCO since 1962.

DAULAT SINGH KOTHARI (Graduates for the developing world) is fifty-eight. He was educated at Cambridge University. He is Chairman of the University Grants Commission, New Delhi and was formerly Scientific Adviser to the Indian Minister of Defence.

BURRHUS FREDERIC SKINNER (New methods and new aims in teaching) is sixty. He was educated at Hamilton College, New York, and at Harvard University. He is now Edgar Pierce Professor of Psychology at Harvard University. He has written *Science and Human Behavior* and *Verbal Behavior*.

BERTRAM VIVIAN BOWDEN (Learning all our lives) is fifty-four. He was educated at Cambridge University. He became Principal of the Manchester College of Science and Technology and Dean of the Faculty of Technology at the University of Manchester in 1953. He is a life peer and was appointed Minister of State for Education and Science in 1964. He has written *Faster than Thought*.

RUTH GLASS (Stability and strife) is Director of the Research Centre for Urban Studies at University College, London. Educated at Geneva and Berlin Universities and the L.S.E. she is an ex-research officer in the Ministry of Town and Country Planning.

MARTIN MEYERSON (Multiple choices) is Dean of the College of Environmental Design and Professor of Urban Development in California University. He has been a consultant to the U.S. Government and served on U.N. missions in Japan and Indonesia. *Margy Ellin Meyerson* (co-author), his wife, is a former Research Director of the American Society of Planning Officials.

DAVID A. MORSE (How much more leisure in 1984?) was born in 1907 and educated at Rutgers University and the Harvard Law School. He was Special Assistant to the U.S. Attorney General, and since 1948 has been Director-General of the International Labour Office in Geneva. He is Chairman of the Board of the International Institute for Labour Studies.

HERBERT READ (Atrophied muscles and empty art) was educated at the University of Leeds. He has held the chair of fine art in the University of Edinburgh and has been Professor of Poetry at Harvard University. He was knighted in 1953. His publications include *The Meaning of Art*, *Art and Society*, *A Concise History of Modern Painting*, and *To Hell with Culture*.

HAROLD MONTAGUE FINNISTON (Gadgets, games, and gambles) is fifty-one. He was educated at the Royal College of Science and Technology, Glasgow. He has been Chief Metallurgist at the Atomic Energy Research Establishment, Harwell, and is now Research Director of C. A. Parsons and Company and Managing Director of the International Research Development Company.

JOAN MAUD LITTLEWOOD (A laboratory of fun) has worked at the Theatre Workshop as artistic director since 1945. She has directed several productions at the Theatre Royal, Stratford East, which have moved to the West End, among them *A Taste of Honey*, *Fings Ain't Wot They Used T'Be*, and *Oh What a Lovely War*. She directed the film *Sparrers Can't Sing*.

LAURENCE DUDLEY STAMP (Footloose industries and the lure of the sun) has been Professor of Social Geography at the L.S.E. and Professor of Geography in the University of London. He is now director of the World Land Use Survey of the International Geographical Union, and has been the British delegate on land use to the Food and Agriculture Organization since 1955.

THORKIL KRISTENSEN (Conceivable patterns of trade) has twice been Minister of Finance in the Danish Government, and has been Professor of Commercial and Industrial Economics in the School of Advanced Commercial Studies at Copenhagen since 1947. He is now Secretary-General of the Organisation for Economic Cooperation and Development.

ERIC WYNDHAM WHITE (Self-sufficiency or interdependence?) is Executive Secretary of the General Agreement on Tariffs and Trade. He has been particularly concerned in efforts to expand international commerce and to reduce trade barriers.

JOHN W. BURTON (Universal non-alignment and methodical decision-making) was Secretary of the Australian Department of External Affairs from 1947 to 1951. He is now researching and teaching international relations at University College, London. He has written *The Alternative* and *Peace Theory*.

JOSEPH ROTBLAT (Scientists as peacemakers) was educated in Poland, and was a member of the British team at Los Alamos during the development of the atomic bomb. He is now Professor of Physics in the University of London. He works for the Pugwash movement, edits *Physics in Medicine and Biology*, and has written *Science and World Affairs*.

MANEKLAL SANKALCHAND THACKER (World development: The crucial choice) was educated at the University of Bristol, and became Professor of Power Engineering at the Indian Institute of Science, Bangalore. He was for eight years Director-General of the Council of Scientific and Industrial Research of India. He is chairman of the UNESCO Natural Science Committee, and the British Commonwealth Scientific Committee.

GEORGE PAGET THOMSON (Coping with 'progress') retired in 1962 after being Master of Corpus Christi College, Cambridge, for ten years. He is a consultant to the Atomic Energy Research Establishment, and Emeritus Professor of Physics in the University of London. In 1937 he was awarded the Nobel Prize for Physics and was knighted in 1943.

LEON BAGRIT (A nation of computer-keepers?) was made chairman of Elliott-Automation in 1963, after being deputy chairman and managing director since its formation in 1957. He organized the first company in Europe devoted to automation. He is a director of Electronic Trust and Technology Investments, and of the Royal Opera House, Covent Garden. He was knighted in 1962.

BARBARA FRANCES WOOTTON (Winners and losers in the rat-race) was educated at Girton College, Cambridge, where she was a director of studies and lecturer in economics for two years. She has been a research officer in the Trades Union Congress and Labour Party joint research department, Principal of the Morley College for Working Men and Women, and Professor of Social Studies at the University of London. She has written many books, and has been a life-peeress since 1958.

GEORGE P. BAKER (Patterns of U.S. industrial development) is George Fisher Baker Professor of Administration at Harvard Business School. He has been Director of the Office of Transport and Communications Policy in the State Department and a member of the U.N. Transport and Communications Commission.

KENNETH FRANKLIN TUPPER (Canada: plenty of room for people) is Vice-President (Scientific) of the National Research Council of Canada. Educated at Universities of Toronto and Michigan, he is a past president of the Engineering Institute of Canada.

LLOYD VIEL BERKNER (The rise of the metropolis) has been president of Graduate Research Center of the South-west, Dallas, Texas, since 1960. Dr Berkner is a graduate in electrical engineering of the University of Minnesota. He is concerned with radio propagation, the structure of the high upper atmosphere, and interactions between the earth and the sun.

TOBIAS LASSER (Soil and schools: The big challenge) is Director of the Botanical Institute at Caracas, Venezuela, and President of the Venezuelan Academy of Mathematics, Physics and Natural Sciences, whose medal he holds.

ABELARDO VILLEGAS (In place of feudalism) is a university professor. He also serves as Secretary of the Committee on the History of Ideas, a section of the Committee of History on the Pan-American Institute of Geography and History.

JOSUÉ DE CASTRO (A continent out of date) is President of the Association Mondiale de Lutte contre la Faim. He was previously Brazilian Ambassador to the United Nations. He has won many awards, including the 1952 Roosevelt Prize, the International Prize of Peace, and the Legion d'Honneur.

FREDERICK TORQBOR SAI (Obstacles and opportunities) is thirty-nine, and was trained in medicine in England and at the Harvard School of Public Health. He has worked for the Ghana Government as deputy chief medical officer, and is now a regional nutrition officer in the African region of the Food and Agriculture Organization. He is also secretary of the Ghana Medical Association.

ROBERT GARDINER (Room for far more people) is fifty, and was educated at Cambridge. He joined the U.N. secretariat in 1946, and has held a variety of posts, among them Officer-in-Charge of the U.N. Operation in the Congo. He has also been on the staff of University College, Ibadan, Nigeria. He is now Executive Secretary of the United Nations Economic Commission for Africa.

DATO SIR ALEXANDER OPPENHEIM (Three fifths of mankind) is sixty-one, and was educated at Balliol College, Oxford. He has been Lecturer in Mathematics in the University of Edinburgh, and Professor of Mathematics at Raffles College, Singapore. He has been vice-chancellor of the University of Malaya since 1957. He was knighted in 1961.

KANAME HAYASHI (Patterns of progress) is seventy, and was educated at Tokyo University. He has been a Professor in Doshisha University, and is now chairman of the Section on Economics, Commerce and

Business Administration of the Science Council of Japan. He is also a Professor at Aichi University. He has translated texts on the theory of money of Marxian economics, and written several books.

JOAN ROBINSON (Prospects for China) is sixty-one, and was educated at Cambridge, where she has been Reader in Economics since 1949. She is the author of *Economic Philosophy* and other books.

ANNE MCLAREN (Optimists versus pessimists) is at the Agricultural Research Council's unit of animal genetics at Edinburgh University. She was educated at Oxford University, where she graduated in zoology and obtained her doctorate for work on viruses of the nerves. She is the joint editor of the biological volume of the Penguin annual Science Survey.

FRANK PRESS (The world of the scientist) is professor of geophysics and director of the California Institute of Technology's Seismological Laboratory. In the period 1961–4 he was a member of the President's Science Advisory Committee, and he is currently on the International Geophysical Year Interdisciplinary Research Panel and Committee for Polar Research.

DESMOND GEORGE KING-HELE (Incineration, inhumanity, or immortality) is a senior principal scientific officer at the Royal Aircraft Establishment, Farnborough, Hampshire. He was educated at Trinity College, Oxford, where he graduated in mathematics.

SIVARAMAKRISHNA CHANDRASEKHAR (A prosperous but unbeautiful world?) is professor of physics at the University of Mysore, where he has been since 1961. Before going to Mysore he worked for two years at the Royal Institution, and before that at University College, London. Professor Chandrasekhar obtained his doctorate for research in crystallography at the Cavendish Laboratory, Cambridge.